Lakeland C

by

E. H. Shackleton, F.G.S.

DALESMAN BOOKS

1991

The Dalesman Publishing Company Ltd.
Clapham, Lancaster LA2 8EB

First Edition, 1966
Reprinted, 1967
Second Edition, 1969
Third Edition, 1971
Fourth Edition, 1973
Fifth Edition, 1975
New impression, 1991
© E. H. Shackleton, 1966, 1991

ISBN: 1 85568 022 X

Printed by Peter Fretwell & Sons Ltd.
Goulbourne Street, Keighley, West Yorkshire BD21 0PZ.

Contents

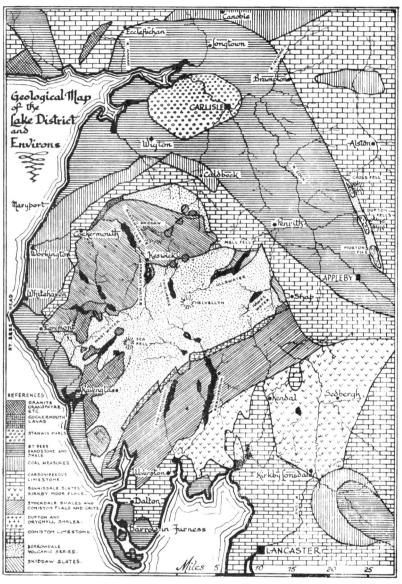

Geological Map of the Lake District and Environs

REFERENCES
GRANITE GRANOPHYRE ETC.
COCKERMOUTH LAVAS
STANWIX MARLS
ST BEES SANDSTONE AND SHALE.
COAL MEASURES
CARBONIFEROUS LIMESTONE.
BANNISDALE SLATES KIRKBY MOOR FLAGS.
STOCKDALE SHALES AND CONISTON FLAGS AND GRITS
DUFTON AND DRYGHYLL SHALES.
CONISTON LIMESTONE
BORROWDALE VOLCANIC SERIES.
SKIDDAW SLATES.

Miles 5   10   15   20   25

—map drawn by E. Jeffrey

Illustrations

Preface

E.H. Shackleton, F.G.S., who died in February 1991, adopted a refreshingly different approach in his book *Lakeland Geology,* first published in 1966. His crede was that the subject could only be properly studied in the field and could never be mastered in the armchair. As *The Advancement of Science* commented at the time of publication:

"Mr. Shackleton has produced just the sort of book which will appeal to the Lake District visitor who wishes to know something of the nature and history of the rocks over which he is walking and who has not had the benefit of a geological training. He has brought a lifetime's geological experience and knowledge of his native Lake District together in a thoroughly refreshing manner. All the author asks is that the visitor keeps his eyes open. From there the reader is informed on all manner of things; local history, folk-lore, as well as descriptions of rocks and minerals and their origin in admirably simple terms. The whole book is admirably conceived and forms a welcome addition to the literature of the Lake District."

Not surprisingly, *Lakeland Geology* proved an instant success and went through five editions in less than a decade. It has become a "classic" of Lakeland literature — hence this reprint of the fifth edition of 1975. The temptations to alter and update the text has been resisted and it stands as a book of its time. Users should bear in mind that some of the locations will have changed, and sadly many sites will no longer be as rich in potential specimens. Geologists should continue to look, learn — and bear in mind the plea which E.H. Shackleton made in his companion volume *Geological Excursions in Lakeland:*

"To the good geologist his hammer is a tool, sometimes a very necessary one let us admit, but it must always be used with a great deal of discretion. It must be remembered that the number of people who take an interest in our rocks, and the science of geology, grows year by year, and it becomes increasingly important that we should preserve what we have. So please, please use your hammer with the utmost discretion, and leave as much as possible for other visitors to enjoy."

— David Joy

1. An Introduction

I HAVE lived most of my life in and around the English Lake District and have always taken a keen interest in its rocks and its scenery. Over the years I have spent much time in teaching the subject of geology to ordinary people and leading geological excursions in the field. As a result of this experience I have concluded that in the teaching of this subject one often has, partly from necessity, to put the cart before the horse. Geology is not, and never can be, successfully mastered in an armchair. A very long time ago a French geologist, Nicholas Desmarest, in teaching his subject, said "Go and see!" I have always found this to be sound advice. One of our own great geologists, the late H. H. Read, once said: "The best geologist is the one who has seen most rocks!" The following pages are an attempt to help the reader at least to make a start.

Few people can be relied upon, after reading geological works, to go out into the field and unhesitatingly point to the things about which they have read. There are many reasons for this. For one thing illustrations in textbooks are almost always specially chosen. They have to be to make clear the point, and yet any practising geologist knows that only rarely does one come across these simplified versions in nature. More often than not there is some complication which has been glossed over in the textbook but is only too confusing in the field. In this book I take the would-be geologist to a precise and definite location and say: "Here at this waterfall you see the water falling over rock. This rock is a granite. Break a small piece off and we will talk about it." In this way you can at least start off without ambiguity. This is an approach I have used myself for many years and I would like to see it more widespread. The method could be applied to any area, but there are few places with so diversified a field as the English Lakes.

Assuming that my reader is not an expert in the subject matter, I suggest that he first reads the introduction and "Some Basic Ideas" followed by "The Building of the Lake District". This will help give him the background. In all probability it will be necessary to return to these chapters from time to time, for they are concentrated stuff and to aid in this a detailed index has been provided. The order in which the excursions are arranged is not haphazard. Deciding on a particular excursion, the reader will be well advised to read it through carefully, trying to locate the points mentioned, and the route, on a map.

The new $2\frac{1}{2}''$ maps are very good for this. If he is really interested he will need a hammer, a lens and a bag in which to carry specimens and in these days these things are readily available in Keswick. Specimens that are worth collecting are worth protecting, so plenty of newsprint is needed in which to wrap them. Before you wrap a specimen write clearly on the paper where you got it, for this will save time and frustration later on. I usually carry a few small boxes when out collecting for really good mineral specimens that are unlikely to survive rubbing one against the other.

Where a specific rock or mineral is mentioned look it up in one or other of the two guides, the one to rocks, the other to minerals. But please . . . do not expect to be able to recognise every specimen you may come across! The rocks and minerals set out in the keys are only the commoner ones; there are literally hundreds of varieties. If, after doing all you can, you fail to identify your specimen, it may well be neither your fault nor mine, but simply that you have found something unusual.

I thank many kind people for their help and encouragement. The late Charles Edmonds, M.Sc., F.G.S., first mooted the idea and helped shape the work, with always the needs of the young people in mind to whose welfare he devoted his life work. To his support and the benefit of his truly encyclopaedic knowledge of rocks and fossils I am truly grateful. His son-in-law, Maurice Branson, B.Sc., F.G.S., kindly read and encouraged me with the first manuscript. Tom Shipp, B.Sc., spent much time on suggested revisions, and my son helped with the drawings. I also extend my thanks to the many students of mine who have helped by checking locations and taking an excursion in MSS to try it out, and the many friends who have helped with photographs. Errors there must be, both of observation and interpretation in a work which tries to cover so wide a field. For these I alone must stand responsible. That the work in its first form has helped to stimulate so much interest in the geology of the Lakes, and in its method of presentation, has given me both much satisfaction and pleasure.

2. Some Basic Ideas

POSSIBLY nowhere else in the world is to be found, in so small an area, such diversified scenery as is to be seen in the English Lake District, where rugged grandeur often alternates with quiet beauty. The geologist's story can add much to the wonder and fascination of our wanderings, though for long there has been no readily accessible guide that could be easily understood by a layman. The expert geologist has the benefit of his fundamental training during which he is almost certain to have seen much of our district. Should he want the details he at least knows where to look, though even he will have to do much searching in a voluminous literature not readily available to everyone, nor by any means free from controversy! What then of the plain man who lacks the training and the time to unravel the long, long story? The following pages are an attempt to guide the enquiring wanderer to places both of interest and of beauty and at the same time to give, as simply as possible, some explanation of what he sees.

What can the geologist tell us that others cannot? Both historian and archaeologist can explain a good deal about what has happened since man first set foot among our hills and dales, but scenic features were already there when first man came. Their help can at best take us back no more than a few thousand years, while the story of the landscape, let alone the rocks which are its bones, must take us back very much further than this. A geologist's province is the study of the earth itself, and more particularly the rocks of which it is made. The geologist's method is to study the changes which the forces of nature are bringing about today and to apply his knowledge to the unravelling of what happened in the past.

Long ago the geologist had arranged all the rocks which had been accumulated in water—the sedimentary rocks—in a relative sequence in order of their age. This he had been able to do by noticing that the remains of living things which had been entombed in the rocks when they were formed, the fossils, became more and more primitive the older the rocks he examined. It was William Smith—the father of British geology—who first made the logical assumption that in any exposure of sedimentary rocks the bed at the top is the youngest and the lowest bed exposed is the oldest. He it was who first found by experience that the same bed when traced across country usually contained the same kind of fossils. Long before geologists could give a really convincing explanation of how all this came to be, they had succeeded in arranging all the sedimentary rocks in a logical sequence and could tell you a good deal about ancient geographies and the kind of life that had lived in the seas of different ages. How all this was done makes a very interesting story which I hope you may be induced to read for yourself. Meanwhile I present a diagram which illustrates the result of all this labour.

The "Geological Column", as it is called, is divided up into sections one above the other. To these are given names, some of which have a slightly familiar ring, like Devonian. This is because much of the early geological work was done in Britain, and even the first three from the bottom—Cambrian, Ordovician, Silurian —although less familiar, are the names of old Celtic tribes that once lived in Wales. It is a fitting monument to the work of our early British geologists that these names are now well known throughout the world. When the layman tries to converse with the geologist he is often disconcerted by the glib way in which the geologist talks in "millions of years". He has good reason for this, and today he speaks with great confidence, which was not always so. I am old enough to remember when the geologist was struggling desperately for time. Even one hundred million years seemed long, but even this not all the physicists would grudgingly allow, while the poor geologist felt it was quite inadequate for all the changes his science visualised.

For long the ages of the different periods were only relative and those now shown in millions of years are a recent addition, given by radio-active determinations. How recent you can perhaps judge when I say that these dates have been extended since this book was written. Today the age of the earth is reckoned in thousands of millions of years and, paradoxically, this estimate we owe to the very physicists who, not so long ago, were sceptical about even one hundred million years! What brought their house tumbling about their ears was the discovery of radio-activity! One of the lines of argument used by the physicist was this: Assuming that our earth had started off in a molten state and that it had steadily cooled ever since then, by carefully measuring the heat given off by the earth, its age could be calculated. When it was discovered that scattered throughout the rocks of the earth there were peculiar elements like Uranium and Thorium which spontaneously generated heat, the argument was seen to be no longer valid, while today not all scientists would agree that our earth was ever molten!

If this new discovery disconcerted the physicist it delighted the geologist, for, looking again at our table, we see that even the Cambrian rocks have a maximum thickness of some 40,000 feet. We have evidence that these rocks were accumulated in comparatively shallow seas from debris swept from the ancient

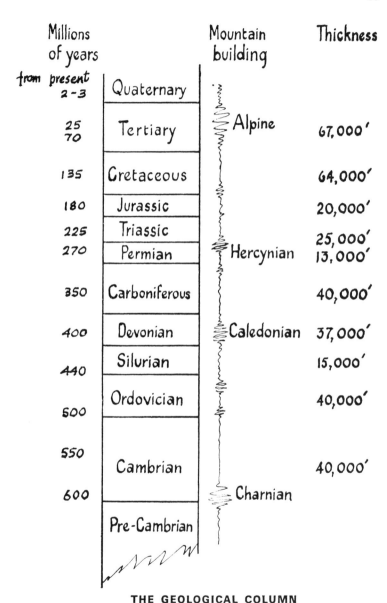

Millions of years from present		Mountain building	Thickness
2-3	Quaternary		
25 70	Tertiary	Alpine	67,000'
135	Cretaceous		64,000'
180	Jurassic		20,000'
225	Triassic		25,000'
270	Permian	Hercynian	13,000'
350	Carboniferous		40,000'
400	Devonian	Caledonian	37,000'
440	Silurian		15,000'
500	Ordovician		40,000'
550	Cambrian		40,000'
600		Charnian	
	Pre-Cambrian		

THE GEOLOGICAL COLUMN

Drawing by H. Shackleton

land surfaces, while the sea bed slowly sank to accommodate it all. It is not difficult to see why the geologist wanted millions of years for such a process. It was Professor Rutherford who first suggested an ingenious way in which the new discovery could be used to yield the ages of the different rock systems. His method, and later refinements of it, is used all over the world today, while further discoveries made since have added substantially to our armoury. Radio-active minerals like Uranium, Rutherford pointed out, spontaneously break down into simpler elements and a very much simplified statement of this process might be put:

$$URANIUM = LEAD + HELIUM + HEAT$$

From which it follows that, in any Uranium mineral, the greater the proportion of lead present, the older the mineral.

Much painstaking research was necessary to find out at what rate this remarkable transformation took place and many disheartening difficulties had to be overcome, but today the fundamental principle is being applied to Uranium and to Uranium-Thorium as well as to other minerals like potassium which, because of their much more widespread occurrence, are proving even more useful. The full technical details of this absorbing discovery are beyond the scope of this book but enough will have been written to show that geologists' time is no longer a matter of guesswork or of pious hope.

Time terms are often used rather loosely; thus a geologist will talk of the Cambrian rocks, or speak of "Cambrian times", meaning the period of time when these rocks were being laid down. To the right of the Geological Column runs a squiggly line which represents the different periods of earth movement, and where the oscillations are greatest we find names like Caledonian and Hercynian. These are the names alike of periods of intense earth movement and the mountains to which the movements gave rise. Caledonian of course refers to the Highlands of Scotland.

Even the old Greek philosophers suspected that our earth had suffered long periods of vigour and decline, but as to the fundamental causes which give rise to these alternating periods we have still no clear idea, and there are many conflicting theories. It is just as difficult to account for the sinking of the sea bed, in such a way that it kept pace with the accumulation of deposits, as it is to account for the forces which crushed and folded these deposits to form enormous mountain chains. The facts themselves are clear enough and just have to be accepted. One result of these movements is that while great thicknesses of sediment accumulated in more or less flat sheets, the following earth movements tilted and folded the beds so that it is comparatively rare to find beds of rock horizontal and quite common to find them inclined or nearly vertical. To find that rocks can be folded and puckered is surprising enough, but it must be emphasized that the process is very slow. It is not surprising, perhaps, to find that rocks subjected to such treatment often break under the strain. These breaks the geologists call "faults".

All mountain building movements seem to be accompanied by the intrusion into the folded sediments of masses of molten material. Often such material never reached the surface at all but slowly cooled and consolidated deep within the earth. Because the cooling was slow, crystals had time to grow and gave rise to beautiful granites, like the one quarried to the east of the district at Shap. If the molten material reached the surface, volcanoes were formed from which lava poured out in sheets, sometimes spreading for miles. In either case the resultant rocks are often called "igneous", literally fire formed, and since the Lake District has suffered from at least three periods of earth movement, rocks of this character are very prevalent.

However much one would like to avoid the technical terms of geological science altogether, this is not really possible. What is possible is to provide some sort of key to the meaning of such terms when they have to be used, and therefore a glossary is provided. Perhaps, after using this book for a while, you will almost unconsciously come to talk like a knight of the hammer yourself!

3.   The Building of the Lake District

OUR story starts with a question mark. Our oldest rocks, the Skiddaw Slates, are held by most geologists now to be of Ordovician age and this would make them about five hundred million years old. But some geologists think that the oldest beds of these Slates are of Cambrian age, and this would make them older still. The deciding factor in an argument like this should be the kind of life remains contained in the rocks. Five hundred million years is a very long time and our Skiddaw Slates have been so crushed and folded that it is not always easy to say which is the right way up of the beds, let alone to determine the remains of the fragile fossils.

Whatever the date we must try to visualise a shallow sea situated off the shores of a great northern continent, the debris from which was being slowly deposited over an area of many hundreds of square miles. We know that the sea bed was unstable because the character of the deposits change from place to place, and with the passage of time. Some are dark mudstones, showing that they were deposited in quiet waters far from land. Some are sandstones or silts, and these were laid down nearer to the sources. Others still are coarse grits with pebbles, and these must have been laid down near to the shore itself. Since these different types of deposit often overlap we can only account for it by earth movement. It may surprise a reader that the sea bed should move up and down in this way. It has happened so often throughout geological time that it is one of the things we must take for granted. Of course changes in the level of the ocean itself are also possible, and this would bring about much the same result, i.e. an advance across, or a retreat of the sea from the shore line.

Although we have many, and widely varying estimates of the thickness of the Skiddaw Slates, let it suffice to say that they are several thousands of feet thick and that their deposition must have occupied many millions of years. Then came a change. It was almost as if the earth shook itself from its long sleep and volcanoes burst through the sea bed to be followed by a long period of vigorous volcanic activity. When a volcano bursts through the earth's crust in this way it does so by forcing a passage through the existing rocks and the explosive violence scatters bits and pieces far and wide. These fragments later consolidate into a rock known to geologists as agglomerate. Through the vent thus formed flows molten lava, and in periods of violent eruption, vast quantities of dust and jagged fragments of solidified lava. This material is often scattered for miles around to form, from the dust, volcanic ash, and from the angular fragments beds of volcanic breccia.

That our Lake District outburst was initially submarine was first suggested by J. F. N. Green about 1920. In time, however, the volcanic cones were built up above sea level for some beds show unmistakable signs of the constituent material having been washed into place. In and around the present area of the Lake District there were, in all probability, many such volcanoes, but we are not sure of the sites of more than a few. One must have been in the vicinity of Keswick, and another, perhaps more definite, at Capel Crag in the valley of the river Calder to the east of Egremont (see *Geological Excursions to Lakeland*).

From these vents, and doubtless from others, spread inter-leaved beds of dark free-flowing lava and beds of ash, tuff and breccias, until many thousands of feet of what are now known as the Borrowdale Volcanic Series were accumulated. Towards the end of this phase the character of the material seems to have altered and the dark free-flowing lavas show a tendency to be replaced by lighter coloured types. Known as rhyolites, these were composed of stiffer lava and when cooled were more glassy; often they show distinct lines of flow and weather with a whitish look. These rocks can be seen around Paddy End, Coniston, in some parts of Langdale, around Bowfell, Scafell Pike and Styhead.

Earth movements followed what must have been a fairly long period of volcanic activity, for the B.V.S. in some places is about 12,000 feet thick. Thus the deposits were uplifted and exposed to the weather but the phase seems to have been of comparatively short duration before the land sank once more beneath the sea. Lying on the weathered edges of the volcanic rocks we find debris from the shore in places, with not infrequently pebbles of lava. Very variable as they are in thickness, content and extent, these beds are found at the base of the overlying Coniston Limestone Series. This Series too is a very variable one consisting as it does for the most part of limy mudstones with here and there more definite bands of limestone. What is interesting is that they contain fossils both in greater number and in a better state of preservation than is usual in the Skiddaw Slates. The graptolites, which were the dominant fossils of the Slates, have been replaced by a completely different fauna consisting of Trilobites, though they are not so easy to find, a great profusion of fossil shells, and for the first time the remains of corals.

In all probability the Limestone Series once covered all our area but they are now found only in a narrow band which runs from Millom and the Duddon, by Coniston and Ambleside and over the fells to Shap. That volcanic activity was not altogether ended is shown by the fact that in some parts beds of ash and lava can be found interspersed with the more normal deposits. As the sea deepened beds of fine black mud were accumulated, crowded with well preserved graptolites. These mudstones, known collectively as the Stockdale Shales, were followed by a vast series of silts, flags and mudstones not unlike the Skiddaw Slates, but the fossils they contain are quite different. These tell us that this series was accumulated during Silurian times. They are known as the Brathay Flags, the Upper and Lower Coldwell Beds, the Coniston Grits and Flags, the Bannisdale Slates and the Kirkby Moor Flags. They cover a wide area in southern Lakeland and reach some 12,000 feet in thickness.

It is easy to say that the deposition of all this material occupied something like one hundred million years, but it is not easy for us to visualise what our words mean! However, to recap: First we have the Skiddaw Slates, then the Borrowdale Volcanics, and this series is overlain unconformably by the Coniston Limestone, all of which are Ordovician (or in part older?) followed by mudstones, flags, grits and slates of Silurian age. The total thickness of this enormous pile can only have been measured in tens of thousands of feet. To these deposits was applied the pressure, from the south-east, of that great earth storm known as the Caledonian movement. The effect of this pressure was to crush our deposits against the north-western continent and the result could be likened to pushing a pile of rugs against a wall.

Our deposits, as we have seen, were by no means all alike. Some, even in their consolidated state, were comparatively soft, others were quite stiff and hard and their reactions to pressure were quite different. The softer beds tended to fold and pucker, the harder beds to fracture and to arch, and this meant not a little relative movement between the two types. Both these results were produced. There was something of a concertina effect with the softer beds thrown into small folds and the whole pushed up into an enormous arch with its axis running N.E . -S.W. through Skiddaw.

This tremendous pressure, exerted over a long time, had other consequences. In most sediments the particles tend to be longer along one axis than along the other and the result of applied pressure is to swing the particles round until their long axes are in line at right angles to the pressure, and usually at a high angle to the bedding. As a result of the pressure and accompanying high temperature, new minerals like mica are formed, the flakes of which also tend to align themselves in a similar way. A rock affected in this way takes on new properties and instead of splitting along the bedding planes, as most sedimentary rocks do, it will split more easily ACROSS them. This new property was first described by our own local geologist, Jonathon Otley, and called "cleavage", and the resultant rock he called a "slate". This is the origin of the Skiddaw Slates, although as a matter of fact cleavage is not very well developed in them. By far the best slates are formed from the ashes and tuffs of the Borrowdale Volcanic Series and these have been worked for roofing slates for ages at Honister, in Borrowdale itself, in Langdale and near Coniston.

During this period of earth movement, which probably went on for millions of years, enormous masses of molten rock material were emplaced in the sediments, usually at the roots of the anticlines. The lovely Shap granite is of this age, and it is assumed that the Skiddaw granite, the Eskdale granite, the Buttermere and Ennerdale Granophyre, as well as the Gabbro of Carrock Fell were all emplaced about this time. If you refer to the "geological column" you will find that the Silurian is followed by the Devonian, which period lasted for about fifty million years. For most of this long period of time land-locked seas, swarming with early forms of fish, existed between the mountain ranges thrust up by the Caledonian earth movements. In many parts of Scotland great beds of conglomerate were formed, while in the north-east beds of sandstone with exquisite fish remains were laid down. But here in Lakeland the whole of the Devonian seems to have been given over to destruction. Under arid desert conditions the rocks of the arch were attacked, broken down and swept away. The most elevated part of the dome, the Silurian, was first to go and this exposed first the Borrowdale Volcanics and then the Skiddaw Slates themselves in the heart of the huge fold.

In this way we were left with a wide outcrop of Skiddaw Slates with, to the north and south, the Borrowdale Volcanics, Coniston Limestone and then the Silurians. Today, to the north, the Silurians are completely buried or have been swept away. Only a little strip of the B.V.S. can be seen. Little remains of the accumulations of rock debris which were formed during this long period of destruction except along the northern shores of Ullswater, at Mell Fell, and possibly in the banks of the Derwent beneath the Cockermouth Lavas. These beds of sandy conglomerate have all the characteristics of the material accumulating today in dry desert conditions.

A short burst of volcanic activity in the Cockermouth area buried this old land surface under about three hundred feet of basalt before the land sank beneath the Carboniferous sea. That our district, even three hundred and fifty million years ago, stood at a considerable elevation is proved by the fact that all round the southern fringe of the area, and along the Vale of Eden, the Carboniferous beds are much older than in the north and west.

In many districts where the beds of limestone lie across the upturned and weathered edges of the older rock, pebble beds are to be seen between the two: the ancient shoreline, as it slowly advanced across the sinking land.

The Carboniferous Limestone is a marine deposit characterised by its fossils. Bands of fossil algae are not uncommon, while corals, fossil shells and crinoids are common, as can readily be seen in many a limestone wall where the fossils have had time to weather out. Although the sea must have been clear for much of the time, for corals like clear water, it was never very deep. This is shown by the occurrence of thin bands of mudstone between the thicker beds of pure limestone. Sometimes the upper surface of the limestone is pitted with potholes, demonstrating that the rock was exposed above the sea, badly weathered, and then sank again for the potholes to be filled with mud or sand. Gradually the sea shallowed and the limestones are followed by the Millstone Grit which, speaking generally, so choked the sea that their surfaces appeared above the waves to be colonised by the enormous peaty forests of Coal Measure times. The coals of the Whitehaven - Maryport coalfield are the remains of these old forests. The fireclays which underlie most of the seams represent the soil in which the forests grew. In the lagoons were freshwater fish and a few molluscs, but it seems that the sea rarely broke in, as the "marine bands" so common and useful as "marker bands" in other coalfields are few in number with us.

The Carboniferous in our part of the world was an uneasy period, rarely free from slight earth movements, and towards the end of the era the deposits were engulfed in the great Hercynian movements which raised mountain chains across Europe, England, Ireland and America. The central core of the Lake District however was highly resistant and the result of this period of earth movement was to raise our rocks into a dome. Because of the resistant core it was a very imperfect dome, broken into blocks by faulting, with renewed movement along old lines of fault, and possibly some deposition of minerals. The summit of this new dome was miles further south than the old arch above Skiddaw and lay somewhere about the Langdales.

History then repeated itself, for a long period of denudation set in under desert conditions, similar in most respects to the conditions in Devonian times. One characteristic of desert deposits is that they are usually red in colour for the iron they contain, owing to the absence of water and organic material, is in the ferric state. The rocks of the Permo-Triassic are often referred to as the "New Red" to distinguish them from the rocks of the Devonian, the "Old Red". The first deposits of the Permian, not surprisingly, are like the Mell Fell deposits, masses of broken rock fragments shot down the scree slopes of the weathering mountains to form a rock known locally as the Brockram. In the cut off arms of the sea, evaporation became so great that what life there was became small and stunted, finally to die out as the concentration became too high to support life. Slowly this highly concentrated matter began to precipitate out and, around the mountains, beds of Magnesian Limestone were laid down to be followed by shales with gypsum and anhydrite. These deposits can be seen at places like Kirkby Thore in the Vale of Eden, or along the coast at Barrowmouth Bay near Whitehaven. In both localities considerable industry has grown around them.

At Barrowmouth (Grid Ref. 956157) at the foot of the cliffs can be seen the current bedded Whitehaven Sandstone, the uppermost part of the Coal Measures, overlain unconformably by the Brockram, then the Magnesian Limestone, and in the cliff the St. Bees Shales. On a little platform above sea level can be seen the remains of old workings from which, long ago, gypsum was mined to make plaster of Paris. Now the anhydrite beds are worked underground on a vast scale for the manufacture of sulphuric acid and cement at the big chemical works close by. The shales themselves, which are also used in the manufacturing process, are overlain by the St. Bees Sandstone, well seen in the nearby St. Bees Head. On the eastern side of the Lake District the Penrith Sandstone shows to a much more marked degree the so called "millet grained" sandstone, the grains of which are almost completely rounded by being blown about the deserts where there was no protecting film of water between the grains. Here at Barrowmouth we have a geological classic illustrating, as it does so well, one of geology's really important phenomena— the unconformity. The Brockram, wherein one can sometimes find pieces of Carboniferous limestone with fossils—derived fossils—as they are called, is here only a few feet thick, but as one goes inland first the Magnesian Limestone, and then the shales, tend to disappear, to be replaced by Brockram which in some of the old mines was found to be three hundred feet thick. The nearer the present fells the thicker the Brockram, which suggests a Permo-Triassic topography not unlike the present— and serves as an illustration of how ancient geographies can sometimes be worked out!

After the many millions of years of the Permo-Triassic the land slowly sank beneath a sea which was becoming thronged with life, life of gigantic proportions, for the Jurassic was the period when the Saurians thrived, along with hosts of squid-like creatures. The Cretaceous saw one of the widest inundations of the land surface ever recorded in the rocks, when immense thicknesses of chalk were laid down in many parts of the world. In other parts of Britain the Jurassic is divided into Liassic and Oolitic: whether these, and the chalk ever covered our Lake

District is not quite clear, but it is at least possible for remains of the first—the Liassic—can be found west of Carlisle.

This great period of deposition lasted for some one hundred and fifty million years at least, to be followed some thirty million years ago by the most recent earth storm, the Alpine, so called because it was during this period of earth movements that the Alps were built, and indeed all the great mountain chains that we know today. The effect in the Lake District was much the same as in Hercynian times, the uplifting of a dome, movement along old faults and the making of a few new ones. On this dome, running roughly from Scafell eastwards across Helvellyn, the forces of destruction immediately set to work. Streams running down on all sides cut deeper and deeper through the new cover until gradually the rocks of the old core were exposed once more.

This new river system, radiating like the spokes of a wheel, reflects the domed structure on which it was initiated but, having cut down to the old core, it bears no relationship to the lie of the old rocks underneath on which it was "superimposed". The river system of the Lake District has become a classic example of "superimposed drainage". Over the better part of thirty million years the carving action of the elements, rain and rivers, gradually shaped our district to something like its present form, modified by a comparatively recent episode with which we can end our story.

Over a million years ago the climate of Britain began to change markedly. The average temperature sank lower and lower until more snow fell in the winter time than summer suns could melt, and snow and ice began to accumulate; the great Ice Age had begun. Naturally the higher land, and the land in higher latitudes, was affected first and so, while glaciers were slowly creeping down the valleys of Lakeland, we suffered an ice invasion from Scotland. This swept across the Carlisle plain, and meeting Lake District ice in the Vale of Eden, turned east over the Tyne Gap and Stainmore to carry Scotch erratics and blocks of Shap granite across Yorkshire to the east coast. Meanwhile the ice, dividing against the Lakeland fells, swept round the west coastal plain, forcing the ice issuing from Lakeland's western valleys to travel side by side with it down across Morecambe Bay into Lancashire and beyond.

Gradually the ice field increased until all the land at least down to a line running roughly from the Wash to the Severn lay, as Greenland does today, swathed in ice and snow thousands of feet thick. Our Lakeland was covered until no more than the highest peaks peeped through, and giant glaciers ground and scoured their way down the valleys. From time to time the climate softened and the ice receded to some extent, only to re-advance and cover the land again. Three such interglacial

periods have been suggested for Lakeland but a correct interpretation is always difficult as each re-advance tends to obliterate
much of the evidence left by the previous recession. For our
present purpose it is sufficient to consider the broad effects on
our district of the work of snow and ice.

The ice, loaded with rock fragments, in its passage had a great
scouring effect. It tended to deepen existing valleys, tear away
outjutting spurs, and thus leave the valleys straighter. In outline
most were changed from the typical V shape of a mountain
river valley to the pronounced U shape of those cut by ice. The
bigger the original valley the greater the over-deepening and the
greater the tendency to leave the side valleys overhanging the
main valleys. Enormous quantities of rock were removed and
carried forward by the ice, much of it to be ground to a stiff
clay which was left as the ice melted. Humps of harder rock
on the valley floors were smoothed and polished on their upstream
sides and plucked on their downstream sides, while pieces of
rock embedded in the ice ground well-marked striations into
the rock surfaces. These can still be seen, perhaps best where
turf or clay has been removed for quarrying.

Some ten to twenty thousand years ago the ice began to melt,
we hope for the last time, but we ought to recognise that we are
in fact still in the Ice Age, and we can have no assurance there
will be no fresh onset! As the ice began to melt, great quantities
of water were trapped and many glacier lakes were formed. To
the west escape for the water was difficult for the Irish Sea was
still piled high with ice, high enough to over-ride the Isle of
Man, so that the water level rose higher and higher until it
escaped south across the fells, cutting in the process many deep
channels still to be seen in the west of the district. These glacial
overflow channels are easy enough to spot because at the present
time they are dry, or if they should have a stream it is obviously
much too small for the channel it occupies.

Into the glacier lakes poured debris-charged water from the
melting ice to build up hummocks of sand and gravel, usually
with noticeably flat tops. These you can see in many places,
particularly down the west coast, and they are very conspicuous
on the northern slopes of Ennerdale. As the Irish Sea ice
retreated up the coast of Cumberland it allowed the meltwaters
to escape to the open sea, cutting conspicuous gaps in the
process, as at St. Bees, Whitehaven, Parton, and Harrington.

The glaciers lingered long in the valleys and on the upland
slopes dumping masses of stiff clay and boulders as the ice
melted down or retreated. Thus many of the overdeepened
valleys were dammed and lakes formed, while at the heads of
the valleys rounded hillocks of waste were left, terminal moraines
like the ones on Honister or at the head of Ennerdale. Some of

these mounds may well have been formed by debris-charged ice melting down in situ. On northern and north-eastern faces of the fells, ice lingered longest of all and by its plucking action hollowed out the many coombs we see today.

There is a good deal of evidence to show that the recession of the ice was accompanied by excessive rainfall. This, helped by meltwater, swept debris down into the dales to fill in parts of the newly formed lakes. In this way Derwentwater and Bassenthwaite were separated. The swollen waters cut valleys too large for the rivers that occupy them today, and this can be very clearly seen between Cockermouth and the sea. Man came north as the ice retreated and many of his primitive tools have been found fashioned from the tough hard volcanics of the district.

It is hoped that this brief outline of the gradual building of our Lakeland. sketchy as it undoubtedly is. may help to explain many of the things you can see for yourself. The map will show you the general plan of the area, the lie of the rocks and the radial drainage.

4.

Keswick, Castlehead and Friar's Crag

KESWICK, at the foot of Skiddaw, has much to recommend it. Not least among its attractions to the geologically-minded are its past connections with the science. Here, in a little court off from the Moot Hall in the main street, Jonathan Otley spent his working life as a watchmaker and established his fame as the first of our local geologists. There is a small plaque upon the wall to commemorate him. Closely associated with men of fame like Sedgwick and Murchison, he was the first man to divide our local rocks up into contrasting series, to give to them names, and to bring some sort of order out of the then chaos. At a later date he was followed by John Postlethwaite who, with his now famous Mines and Mining in the Lake District, first recorded the many interesting connections of the district with mining activity.

The science of geology is first and foremost a matter of observation. One of the things which takes the eye of the practised man is how things are built. By looking closely at such prosaic things as walls and buildings he can oftimes learn much about the local rocks. In the old days any kind of building was a matter of hard labour and not unnaturally the builders sought for the most readily available material. First, of course, they had to dig for foundations, and since in Keswick the ground is invariably composed of glacial drift, many walls and old buildings are built of stones taken from the drift. You can easily recognise such work from the stones themselves. Of various shapes and sizes, and many colours, they are usually smooth and at least partly rounded. You can see them very well in some of the old passages that lead from the main street to the car park behind the police station. Recent years have seen many changes in the little town and, if many of the older buildings which used Skiddaw Slate are gone, much use has lately been made of the green ashes from the Borrowdale Volcanics. Cut and polished these stones, especially when they are wet, show to perfection the fragmentary nature of the material ejected from our local volcanoes of long ago. Many of the stones built into the walls are very rough and this is due to the marked cleavage which affects most of our rocks here-abouts. If you want them square and clean cut you have to cut them, for they rarely break that way!

In the market place stands the Moot Hall. It bears a green

stone plaque on the wall above the steps but the information is a little misleading. It is quite true that an old Court House once stood upon this site. True, too, that it was partly rebuilt in 1571 —but not as a Court House and prison. This date takes us back to a very interesting period in the history of Keswick; about 1565 the little place was invaded by German miners brought to Keswick by Elizabeth I to exploit local mineral wealth. Copper became the main objective and in 1571 Richard Dudley of Yanwath "—took for ten shillings the year of the old Lady Radcliffe the Court House—pretty ruinous". This he rebuilt as the Queen's Receiving House for copper, and here the copper ingots produced by the German smelters received the "Queen's mark". That he ever got paid for his rebuilding of the old Court House I very much doubt, but then Richard was a relative of Lord Robert Dudley, the Queen's favourite. His lovely old house, the pele tower of Yanwath, still stands just outside Penrith.

Not far away stands the *George,* probably the oldest inn in Keswick. It too bears a plaque recording that it was a favourite meeting place of the German miners and the Queen's representatives. Daniel Heckstetter, the leader of these German adventurers, stayed for a time at the *George* until he got a house of his own in the little town. Smelting furnaces were built out at Brigham by the river Greta and in their hey-day were considered "the finest works of their kind in Europe". Nothing of this now remains except a tunnel through the rock, cut by stope and feather, which carried water to the waterwheels.

Walking about Keswick it is still possible to see other evidence of the town's close connection with mines and mining. On many a gatepost and garden wall you will see beautiful mineral specimens. There are some on the Penrith road leading out of town, and there are others on the back road that leads by the Heads from Lake Road to the bus station. A word of caution is needed here, however. Specimens of lead and zinc or barytes are likely to be local, but the lovely cubes of yellow and purple fluor-spar are not. Flour-spar is an uncommon mineral in the lakes proper and these specimens are far more likely to have come from the nearby Alston area. Probably these specimens go back to the time when the decline of local mining forced the Keswick miners to look further afield. Our local miners in the old days thought little of tramping to Nenthead or Alston to find employment for their skills, in much the same way as for generations they walked the Sticks Pass over Helvellyn to work at Greenside in the lead mines.

Forsaking the subject of mines and mining for the moment, let us leave the town by the Borrowdale road and proceed to Castlehead. The climb up from the road through the woods to the top is not great but, for our purpose, is well worth making; there can scarcely be a better place to begin geological excursions in the district. Near the summit the trees thin out and the last few steps are in actual rock. If you have a hammer a hard blow will strike off a small piece of dark material which is dolerite. The word means "deceptive" because of the many forms this rock can take, but it always has a common origin—it is igneous. It came to its present resting place in a molten form. Even examined with a lens there is not much to see, for the rock has undergone much alteration. There are little crystals of a mineral called augite, a little mica and for the rest, alteration products. As you stand on this summit you are standing, according to some geologists, on the site of one of the old volcanic vents, and the dolerite is what is left of the lava that plugged the vent.

Look now to the north, where Skiddaw rears its head 3,000 feet above the sea. Notice its graceful slopes and rounded outline and turning now to the west, note the similar peaks of Grisdale Pike, Causey Pike and Grassmoor, with the smooth outline of Catbells in the foreground across the lake. All these have been carved from the softer Skiddaw Slates and contrast sharply with the precipitous crags of Walla and Falcon at your back. These, the Jaws of Borrowdale, Great End and Scafell range beyond, are all shaped from the tough lavas and ashes of the Borrowdale Volcanic Series; it is the work of the weather on these contrasting rock types which gives us the pleasing variety of our Lakeland scenery.

The more discerning might be tempted to ask why Skiddaw, made of comparatively softer rocks, should overtop the crags of harder volcanics at its back, and rear its head practically as high as Scafell itself? A sound question, but you will remember that for millions of years the slates of Skiddaw were themselves protected by a tough layer of the volcanics. Not until these had been worn away could the weather get at the softer slates.

Look now at Derwentwater with its wooded shores and islands. It is comparatively shallow, and like Bassenthwaite with which it was once continuous, owes its origin to a huge moraine left by the melting ice across the outlet of the valley. Sometimes, after long continued rain, the two lakes unite in one great sheet of water as they did before the stream, washing the loose rubbish left by the ice from the fells, filled in the lake to leave the low lying plain between. If you look now at the head of the lake you will see that there too, a stretch of low lying marshy ground is steadily encroaching upon the waters of the lake; all this in not much more than ten thousand years, but ten thousand years of quite exceptional conditions. It is one thing to sweep away loose clay and stones; quite another to remove solid rock itself.

Some idea of the effect of weather on solid rock can be obtained by looking at Walla and Falcon Crags. Beneath the precipitous

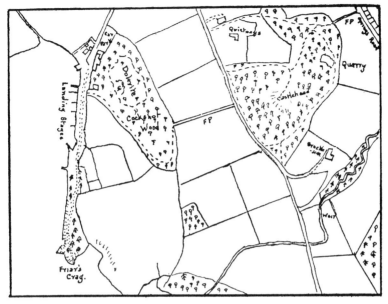

Rough Sketch Map of Friars Crag, Castlehead
and Cockshot Wood.

line of the crags long slopes of scree, broken rock material, run down to the tree clad slopes beneath. It is quite certain that this scree was not there when the ice was grinding its way down the dale. It has all accumulated since by the action of the weather, heat and cold, wind and rain, and the downward pull of gravity, those same forces that over millions of years have carved out the jewel of the Lakes and are still at work around us.

As we walk quietly down from the summit, watch for a turning in the path that leads away from the lake. This path leads through a gate and across the fields to Springs road, but before reaching the gate turn to the right and this will bring you shortly to an old quarry where you can easily obtain a much fresher specimen of dolerite than was possible above. Notice that the rock is cut through by veins and stringers of a white mineral, this is calcite. If you now follow the path round the Head in the direction of the road you will come to a place where the path divides with a pile of erratic blocks near the junction (Grid Ref. 270226). Perhaps this is a convenient place to consider our Castlehead as the site of an ancient volcano. The crags of Walla and Falcon, backed by Blaeberry Fell, in spite of their height of some 2,000 feet, by no means represent the total thickness of volcanic material which once accumulated here, for much of it has since been swept away. In what still remains there are many beds of lava, and even much of the volcanic ash probably issued in an incandescent state. If the dolerite plug of Castlehead represents the vent, then this vent passed up through Skiddaw Slate which, beneath the drift, surrounds the dolerite. One would expect that the passage of so much highly heated material through the vent over a very long period of time would have altered the slates for a considerable distance. However, if you now cast around a little from where you are standing besides the blocks of stone you should be able to find an outcrop of the slate showing little, if any, alteration. Convenient as it would be to point airily to Castlehead as the site of our ancient volcano, I am afraid it was never quite so simple as that!

Leaving this problem for the moment, let us cross the road and take the footpath that leads down to the lake and Friar's Crag. At the end of the crag where you can stand and gaze down the lake to the Jaws of Borrowdale, notice that the rock at your feet is rather like the rock we have just examined on Castlehead. A bit knocked off with your hammer will confirm this, for dolerite it certainly is, and for long the crag has been regarded as an offshoot from Castlehead. In this case the intrusion takes the form of a "dyke", a north country term for a wall. This is just what the crag is: a wall-like body of dolerite intruded into the Skiddaw Slates. If in making your return towards town you get down on to the lake shore (assuming the water is not too high) and walk towards the boat landings, a little hammering will show you dolerite, with the slate close in contact altered by the heat until it is hardened and somewhat bleached. A little further away you can find unaltered Skiddaw Slate.

At the end of the boat landings there is now a café and the path down which we came from Castlehead. Exploration in the wood behind the buildings will show another body of dolerite of rather indefinite shape, at least in summer when vegetation tends to hide much of the exposure. I have no doubt that this mass is in contact with the dyke we have just left and it is interesting to note that across the lake at Rosetrees, on what is now Lady Rochdale's estate, there is yet another similar exposure. Almost one hundred years ago H. Allayne Nicholson of Penrith, one of our early Lakeland geologists, claimed that Friar's Crag was connected not with Castlehead but with Rosetrees. Although some recent work has been done nothing so far has been published, but I wonder if all these separate exposures were not once feeders to a volcano, the cone of which once covered much of this area but has since been completely swept away!

5.

The Volcanics of Cat Ghyll

L EAVING Keswick by the Borrowdale road, travel past Castle-head until you are opposite the gap between Walla and Falcon Crags. Here a rocky stream passes under the road to flow into the lake, this is Cat Ghyll. If you follow this stream down towards the lake, keeping on its southern bank, you will notice in several bluffs and outcrops a rock of reddish purple colour. This innocent looking rock is worthy of your attention. It was for long a bone of contention.

Professor Marr called it "purple Breccia", and he went on to describe it as a fault breccia, i.e. a rock made up of angular fragments of broken rock due to breaking and crushing along a line of fault. In the elucidation of the geological structure of any area it is necessary to form some theory as to what happened—how, and when—and the Professor believed that in the building of the Lake District the rocks of the area had been faulted on an enormous scale, with the production of great bands of shattered rock. It is dangerous to hold any theory too steadfastly, for by doing so one is apt, all unconsciously more than likely, to weight the evidence in favour of one's theory. Perhaps this is what happened here. There is a fault and a fault breccia as we shall see, but the purple breccia was re-examined by J. F. N. Green about 1918 and interpreted by him as an explosion breccia.

This takes us back to the time when our local volcano was first establishing itself and a close examination of this rock will show that it consists of angular fragments in a fine purple base. Many of these fragments are volcanic, but some are undoubted pieces of Skiddaw Slate, the country rock through which the vent was blasted. That some of the fragments are quite large suggests that the vent, wherever it was, was not far away. The purple base consists of a fine volcanic glass.

On the very edge of the lake stands a rocky bluff some one hundred and twenty yards south of where the stream enters the water. Going round this to the southern side make your way along the face until you find a small cave or hole in the rock. If you examine this exposure carefully you will find it to consist of hard grey slate. In and around the hole it is made up of large angular broken fragments cemented together. If the level of the lake is not too high an excellent exposure is to be seen low down at the right hand side of the crag (standing with your back to the lake).

Here you are on the actual line of fault which divides the Skiddaw Slates to the west from the Borrowdale Volcanics to the east. The exposure itself is mostly composed of fault breccia. This exposure is both interesting and unusual for here you can see the line of fracture, or fault, and this is not too common. In and around Lakeland there must be hundreds of faults but only rarely does one see the line of breakage. In mines, yes, but on the surface not nearly so often as textbooks may be thought to imply. Very often faults have to be inferred from the fact that the strata do not match up, or from some sudden change in topography for which there seems no immediate cause.

Return now to the road immediately above the bluff and directly opposite, on the other side of the road, a stile gives access to Falcon Crag. Along the fell side of the road the rocks have been cut through in the making of the road. On this rock face, some thirty paces from the stile, you can see a pocket in the purple breccia filled with reddish shales. They are quite well bedded and have obviously been laid down in water during the period when the explosive breccia was accumulating. Such a pocket would be difficult to account for if the surrounding rock were indeed a fault breccia. A little further along the rock wall is a large and unmistakable fragment of Skiddaw Slate entombed in its purple base.

If the stream is not in spate you can now enter the bed of the ghyll and begin to follow one of the best known sections of the Borrowdale Volcanics in the district. It is a geological classic and was first worked out by Clifton Ward of the Geological Survey.

I find the first exposure, above where the stream passes under the road, a little puzzling. It has every appearance of being Skiddaw Slate but it seems to be entirely surrounded by purple breccia. It is true that it is not a normal Skiddaw Slate, for it contains many fragments that suggest a volcanic origin, but it is bedded and is certainly different from the surrounding rocks. If indeed it is the Slate it seems to suggest again that the breccia was not laid down without interruption.

Following the ghyll upwards you will encounter many water-falls, the rocks of which are the same purple explosion breccia and in some of them, where the water has cleaned and polished the rock, the angular fragmentary nature can be very well seen. The series of falls is followed by a quieter section where expo-sures are not so good but boulders suggest that the nature of the underlying rock has changed, for the purple breccia has been replaced by grey-green ashes. While the ground in this section is not level it is far less steep than in the previous section and this is due to the fact that the ash beds are not nearly so tough and resistant to the weather as either the underlying breccias or the overlying lavas. This step-like nature of the volcanic country is something that might be looked for; it is a marked feature and is due to the differing resistance to erosion of the beds of

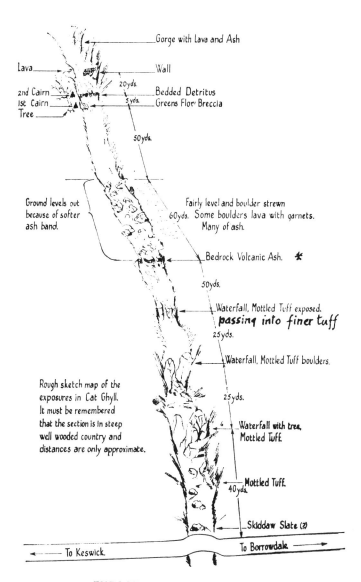

Gorge with Lava and Ash

Lava

Wall

2nd Cairn
1st Cairn
Tree

20yds.

5yds.

Bedded Detritus
Greens Flor Breccia

50yds.

Ground levels out
because of softer
ash band.

Fairly level and boulder strewn
60yds. Some boulders lava with garnets.
Many of ash.

Bedrock Volcanic Ash.

50yds.

Waterfall, Mottled Tuff exposed.
passing into finer tuff
25yds.

Waterfall, Mottled Tuff boulders.

Rough sketch map of the
exposures in Cat Ghyll.
It must be remembered
that the section is in steep
well wooded country and
distances are only approximate.

25yds.

Waterfall with tree,
Mottled Tuff.

Mottled Tuff.
40yds.

Skiddaw Slate (?)

To Keswick

To Borrowdale

EXPOSURES IN CAT GHYLL

Drawing by H. Shackleton

ash and lava. Although this part of the section is usually boulder-strewn there was an exposure of ash last time I examined it just where the stream bends and begins to fall more rapidly.

Above this quieter section the stream issues from a gorge, but before venturing into this I would like you to pay some attention to the stream bed below the wall. At the foot of a tree on the north bank I have built a cairn and immediately below it, in the stream bed, a large slab of rock can be seen. It is exceedingly tough and is composed of grey-green fragments cemented into a fine base. When the slab is wet the detail shows much more clearly. Originally this was described as volcanic breccia and was thought to be made up of fragments blown from the vent. It was J. F. N. Green who first claimed that this rock was in fact a lava, the brecciation he described as "autobrecciation" due to the fact that the lava was extruded under the sea.

The hot lava flowing from the vent would naturally be chilled at its surface by contact with the sea water and instantly con-solidated, but as it flowed on, this chilled surface layer would be broken up. Solid lava, however, is heavier than the same lava in liquid form, so the fragments would sink back into the liquid and become incorporated with it. Repetition of this process has produced the rock you are now examining and careful scrutiny will show that the edges of some of the fragments have been re-absorbed.

Green's views were not readily accepted but, taken as a whole, they do make sense. Sub-aerial lavas usually have a scoriaceous or cindery surface due to the escape and expansion of gases from the fluid mass. A single lava flow examined in detail generally shows the steamholes increasing in size and number towards the upper surface. In many of the Borrowdale lavas there is no such increase, while scoriaceous surfaces are often absent. Basaltic flows exuded at the surface will flow for miles but andesitic lavas are much stiffer because they contain more silica, and so do not normally flow so easily, yet individual flows in the Borrowdale Series can often be traced for miles. What stops sub-aerial lavas from flowing is the loss of volatiles, gases and most of all, steam.

Extruded under a considerable depth of water, Green points out, the pressure over the lava could very well equal, or nearly so, the vapour pressure within. In such case little expansion of steam bubbles would be possible and such vesicles as there were would tend towards a greater uniformity in size; and since the volatiles were mostly retained the flow would be capable of much greater lateral spread than would be the case with the same lava flowing sub-aerially. That lavas can advance quietly under water without the violent explosion one would naturally expect may seem extraordinary but this has been observed in various parts of the world. The lava flow from Torre del Greco near Naples was watched from a boat. Giorgios Island at Santorin composed of molten lava, rose quietly from the sea in 1886.

On the bank of the stream, some five yards above the first, stands a second cairn. Opposite this a band of greyish rock crosses the bed of the ghyll. The band is not very thick but the rock of which it is composed shows clear signs of having been deposited in water. It is **bedded** and close examination shows it to be composed of volcanic detritus, no doubt washed into place from some nearby cone which at this time must have reared its head above the waves.

Examine the rocks at the entrance to the gorge. They are composed of dark green lavas, very hard and tough and here showing no signs of brecciation or vesicularity. Careful search however should show on freshly broken surfaces little globules of a pale lilac colour. These are almadine garnets and they are by no means uncommon in the rocks of the Borrowdale series, lavas and ashes alike. Sometimes they are so small as to require a microscope to make them out, but often they attain the size of peas. The explanation of their presence is not simple. Usually garnets are found in rocks which have been subjected to very great pressure, like some of the rocks of the Scottish Highlands, or in rocks which have come from very great depths in the earth's crust. Their presence in the rocks of the Volcanic Series has given rise to a great deal of argument, but with no very satisfactory conclusion.

Unless you are very active and do not mind a bit of rough scrambling it is better to follow the path round the left-hand shoulder of the gorge. The gorge itself, if you follow it, shows a succession of lavas and ashes, not always easy to distinguish one

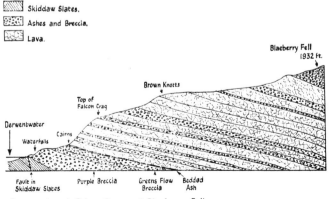

Section through Falcon Crag and Blaeberry Fell.

(After J.C.Ward F.G.S. with modifications by E.H.Shackleton F.G.S.)

from another. Above the gorge the path runs out on to a steep scree slope at the foot of which, in the bed of the ghyll, you may find a lava showing very fine steam holes filled with chalcedony and tiny agates, while a little further upstream you may find boulders of a very beautiful fault breccia. It comes from a fault which runs up the steep chasm to the left. The lava which forms the top of Walla Crag is well known for its vesicularity. Here can be found a pale green mineral, often in clumps of radiating needles; this is Epidote. Agates, Carnelians and Jaspers are all reported from here.

If you wish to complete the section it is best to cross over the swampy ground above Walla and walk south for about half a mile before climbing the slopes of Blaeberry Fell. Apart from some of the beds shown as "breccia", which are in fact brecciated lavas, the appended section due to Clifton Ward is very good but by no means easy for an amateur to follow in detail. Finally, over the last 40 years or so, the lower reaches of Cat Ghyll have become much encumbered with large boulders. Perhaps a better place to see flow breccias in situ is on the Grey Knotts side of Gillercoomb, where some of the Wrengill Andesites show this structure very well.

N.B. Here we are confronted by great changes wrought by floods. How long the present exposures will last it is impossible to say, but these notes were made in March, 1969. Some eighty paces from the road there is an exposure in the bank. This is not a flood exposure but it is worth noting. A small bluff is split conspicuously down the middle by a deep cleft. To the north the bluff consists of purple breccia but the rock on the stream side of the cleft consists of fine tuff with a current bedded wedge on the corner. (Don't, please don't hammer it away!).

Some thirty paces above the bluff, at a small fall, purple breccia can be seen to pass into fine tuff with pink fragments. The stream now swings sharply to the north and flows over a flat pock-marked pavement. This looks suspiciously like the flow brecciated No. 1 Lava. The slab of flow breccia is still exposed by the first cairn but can now be seen to be a boulder, not bed rock.

The exposure at No. 2 cairn has me puzzled. There is now an exposure several feet thick of grey-green ash, but the "sedimentary ash band" talked about by both Marr and myself has completely disappeared, apparently covered up by tons of debris swept down the ghyll. (By the way, the grey-green crystals in the lava at the entrance to the gorge are augites, or decomposition products after augite. I make mention of this because, looking at the lava recently, the augites seemed more conspicuous than the tiny garnets.)

As no trace of this interesting exposure can now be found, I propose to deposit a specimen from it in the Keswick Museum.

6. Excursion to Borrowdale

I THINK it would be wise to allocate to this excursion a full day. There is much to see, and one needs time to appreciate things, more particularly if these things are entirely new. Take the boat from the boat landings across to Brandlehow where, on arrival, you will see some partly overgrown mine tips. This is the site of a very old and interesting mine, the Brandley. When it was first worked no one seems quite sure. We do know it was worked before the days of gunpowder, and that takes us back to before the days of Elizabeth I. Many of the older parts of the mine have galleries which are little wider than the vein itself, and what rock was cut away was removed by "stope and feather". These old mining implements were about five or six inches long and made from pieces of iron. The "feathers", from one half to one inch broad, were round on the outside, flat on the inside and tapered to a point. The "stope" (more commonly called the "plug" these days, for the device is still used!) was a thin tapering wedge of about the same length as the feathers. A hole was first bored into the rock with a hammer and "jumper" in much the same way as we today use a rawlplug drill (but I doubt if it was as easy to do!). Into this hole the feathers were introduced with their flat sides together and parallel as near as possible with the grain of the rock. The thin edge of the stope was then inserted between the flat faces of the feathers and driven home with a hammer. In this way the piece of rock was riven off. It must have been both time consuming and a form of very hard labour, for the old men never removed any more rock than was absolutely necessary!

During the long life of the Brandley mine large quantities of lead and zinc ore were won from the veins, the run of which you can see for yourself if you follow with your eye the line of tips and adits which run up the slopes of Cat Bells. A little search among the rubble on the tips should provide specimens of the minerals worked. The procedure is quite simple. Seat yourself comfortably by one of the tips and, picking up pieces of rock, try their weight. Sooner or later you will find a piece that feels rather heavy for its size, and breaking this with your hammer you may well find silvery cubes of lead ore, or galena. Possibly on the same piece you may see splotches of a dark brown colour; this is the ore of zinc, zinc blende or sphalerite. Should this game interest you at all there are many places in the Lake District where minerals—about one hundred and twenty different kinds—can be found. Here at Brandlehow you might find cerussite, or "white lead ore"—a carbonate of lead which occurs in long white needles. This interesting mineral only occurs sparingly but is sometimes found on breaking up bigger pieces of waste. You are unlikely to find the gold which legend associates with the mine!

If your wanderings bring you near to any of the open adits it is as well to remember that, even with adequate light, the exploration of old mine workings is rather hazardous and not to be undertaken lightly. Apart from pockets of foul air, the adits which run up the hillside are usually connected underground by vertical shafts; or often the ore has been completely worked out between one level and the next. To stumble into one of these traps unawares can lead to a nasty fall and prove disastrous, and may well endanger someone else in an effort to rescue you!

There are many old mines in the Lake District, over the fell in the next valley of Newlands and particularly in the Caldbeck Fell area. The wealth that came from them gave rise to the old saying "Caldbeck and Caldbeck Fells be worth all England else". What is the origin of these mineral veins? Most of the veins of the district, like the one you see here at Brandlehow, run steeply up the fell sides and a little experience soon teaches one that most of them were originally lines of fault. "Fault rock", as the miner calls it, or more correctly "fault breccia", rock broken into angular fragments and often cemented together by quartz, lead, zinc or the white barytes, is of common occurrence and should be sought on the tips in the wood. Sometimes the walls of the vein, as seen underground, are smooth, polished or striated by the slipping of the rocks, for the vertical displacement can be anything from a few inches to several hundred feet. This displacement is known as the "throw" of the fault and it is interesting to note that faults with a very big displacement are rarely well mineralized. It would seem then that the lines of weakness presented by faults are in some way transformed into mineral veins, and yet there are hundreds of faults in and around Lakeland that show little or no sign of mineralization. It is true that faults provide the lines of weakness, but the source of the minerals themselves must be sought elsewhere. Generally speaking most mineralization is to be found in close proximity to great igneous masses, usually of the "acid" or granitic type rather than the "basic" igneous rocks like the dolerite of Castlehead.

When great granite masses cool and crystalize there are some elements which will not fit easily into the lattices of the growing crystals, such elements as chlorine, boron and sulphur, and particularly the latter. These highly active elements pick up the metallic elements like lead, zinc and copper, and carry them away in a gaseous form, or dissolved in superheated water. These gases and solutions—"emanations" as they are often called—find their way along the faults where contact with the cold rocks slowly cool them and cause the minerals to be precipitated. If there is plenty of room, beautiful crystals are formed to provide some of the lovely specimens you may see in the Keswick Museum.

These cavernous openings in the veins are known to the miners as "vugs", "loughs" or "druses", and the writer well remembers entering as a lad one such lough in the Force Crag mine. It was the size of a small room, lined from floor to ceiling with purest white barytes, and resplendent with glittering crystals of sphalerite which shimmered like diamonds in the light of our acetylene torches. It is from such places as these that the best mineral specimens are to be got. To get them in perfect condition often requires both much time and patience. The miner, however, is not mining for specimens—what he wants is ore—so specimens that would delight you and me are often thrown out on to the tips. Many are ruined by such treatment, but some survive and can be found by patient search. You may be lucky enough to find something for yourself!

The real bugbear of Lakeland mining has always been water and this is the real reason why most mines are found running up the fell sides—they were self draining. Only when this ore had been worked out did they begin to go down and then water had to be pumped from the workings. In the old days when the only power for working pumps came from waterwheels many mines had to be abandoned. Brandley was so abandoned and, so it is said, was only restarted when one of the first steam pumps ever to come north was erected here. One peculiarity of this mine is that the water from it contains an appreciable amount of salt. Both calcium chloride and sodium chloride are present, along with small amounts of magnesium chloride and sulphate. The water has been used medicinally from time to time in the past. What is puzzling is the source of these salts. There are no salt deposits as such for many miles in any direction, and the only other possible source, volcanic, seems a bit unlikely. It is true that salt solutions and warm waters are often associated with dying vulcanicity but there is little evidence of such activity in our area since Carboniferous times, unless there were deep seated disturbances during the mountain building movements of Tertiary times, and even this is some thirty million years ago.

This mine had yet another peculiarity, and one that gave rise to many difficulties in the working of the mine. Much of the quartz, which often occurs as the "gangue" or veinstone, and is usually a pure white hard substance, was here found as "friable quartz". Instead of its usual tough hard form it was more like sugar, or a white sand, and while this made it easy to extract the

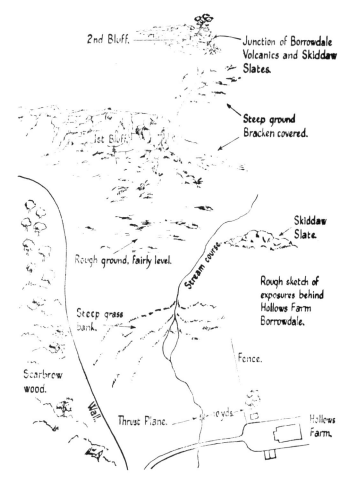

2nd Bluff.

Junction of Borrowdale Volcanics and Skiddaw Slates.

Steep ground Bracken covered.

1st Bluff.

Skiddaw Slate.

Rough ground, fairly level.

Stream course

Rough sketch of exposures behind Hollows Farm Borrowdale.

Steep grass bank.

Fence.

Scarbrow wood.

Wall.

Thrust Plane.   10 yds

Hollows Farm.

Drawing by H. Shackleton

ore, you extracted it at constant risk of being buried alive by the friable quartz!

Leaving Brandlehow we will make our way down to the little hamlet of Grange in Borrowdale. Standing on its lovely old bridge, notice that the side nearest to the houses is built upon a beautifully rounded rock. Notice, too, that it is scored by deep striations running parallel to the babbling Derwent. The rock is a "Roche Moutonee" so called from a fanciful resemblance to a sheep's back as it lies in the field. It is a rock exposure which has been ground smooth by ice and striated by stones frozen into the sole of the glacier which once ground its way down Borrowdale.

Leaving the bridge go back into the hamlet and take the lane on the left opposite the church. A few minutes' walk along this rough lane will bring you through a gate and out into the open. Take the track to the right that leads to Hollows Farm. now a Youth Hostel. If you pass the time of day with the warden and ask his permission to go up the fell side he will gladly give it; it may be useful too, for he knows where the exposure is that we are going to see, and it isn't easy to find. In the field immediately behind the outhouse a small stream tumbles down the fell side. Ten yards from the corner of the outhouse you will find a place where the water slides across bed rock. This is the scored surface of a very low angled fault, or thrust plane, and is one of the places where the rocks slipped bodily over one another during earth movements.

Although comparatively small this is an interesting exposure. In the early days of Lakeland geology thrust planes were very much to the fore. Such thrusts had been discovered in the Alps and in the Highlands of Scotlands, some of them of enormous size. The Matterhorn, for instance, has been moved bodily across country for many miles on such a thrust plane, and some geologists were expecting to find them in our Lakeland. Professor Marr seemed to believe at one time that there were no normal junctions between the Skiddaw Slates and the succeeding Borrowdale Volcanics. All such junctions were either faults or thrust planes.

If you now scramble up the fell, bearing left to where the ground becomes rough and craggy, you will find the rocks standing up on end. The crags to your left, as you stand facing the fell, are Borrowdale Volcanics. while the more open ground to the right has many outcrops of Skiddaw Slate. The actual junction of the two series runs down the right hand edge of the second bluff up the fell side, immediately below and slightly to the right of the holly tree. Here on the sloping surface a patch of B.V.S. has weathered almost white and the junction line shows clearly against the brown of the Skiddaw Slates. You will be able to see where geologists have broken off pieces of the rock trying to get a specimen of the two rocks side by side on the one piece.

In this exposure you can see the two series lying side by side without any sign of a break. Originally the B.V.S. overlay the Slates but earth movements and faulting has since displaced the exposure but without really obscuring their relationship. Incidentally fossil shells have been found within a few inches of the junction on the Slate side. In the Volcanics there are no fossils.

Perhaps only geologists will appreciate the importance and full significance of this exposure but at least you have seen a bit of classic ground which caused a good deal of controversy when this was the only place known where such a junction could be seen. Despite the fact that other similar exposures have since been found, the controversy as to whether the two series succeed one another conformably or not still continues.*

Return now to the lane from which you started, but instead of going back to Grange continue towards the Jaws of Borrowdale. Coming to the river you will see a group of trees almost surrounded by water. Here we might pause and consider the work of rain and rivers. I can remember the time when these trees grew upon the river bank, but the river has eaten the ground away here while piling up a bank of pebbles on the opposite bank. Looking up and down stream notice that the river is tending to swing from side to side, cutting into the bank on one side and piling up pebble beds on the other. Now look carefully at the stream itself and you will find that it runs more swiftly against the bank and more slowly by the pebble beds.

The power of a stream to cut depends upon its velocity, the speed at which it flows. The faster it flows the more stones and grit it can carry, and it is what the water carries that does the cutting. When the water slows down on the inside of a bend it has in consequence to drop some of its burden. It builds up the bed of gravel and pebbles as you can see, and this tends to throw the water (and its burden) still more against the bank, which as a result is undercut and slowly moves back. Sooner or later it will meet something in the bank which it cannot easily move, perhaps a very large boulder or solid rock, and then the stream will swing back against its own pebble beds. These it will proceed to move downstream to pile them up again at the first stretch of slack water.

This is HOW a stream cuts from side to side, but why does it do this? Why does it not just continue to cut down and down? We have seen that the stream's power to cut comes, not from the water, but from what the water carries. and what the water can carry depends upon the rate at which it flows. Where the slope is steep, the rate of flow is fast, and so is the rate of erosion. Where the land flattens out the rate of flow lessens and the stream tends to drop some of its burden. In the case we are examining the river flows into Derwentwater, so its "base level", as it is called, is fixed. Below the level of the water in the lake, the Derwent cannot cut; its ability to cut down is checked. Nevertheless the stream has energy and this it uses to cut from side to side forming meanders. A river that does this is said to be in its "plain stage", for a plain is the outcome of its activities, given time.

* See "Geological Excursions in Lakeland"

On old continental land surfaces this process of erosion has gone on for a very long time and gradually all outstanding features tend to be eroded away; hill country is reduced and cut back, and slowly a plain known as a "peneplain" is produced. The base level in this case is the sea, and if a profile of such a river system from its source to the sea were to be plotted it would give a close approximation to a logarithmic curve. So far as I know no English term has ever been applied to this curve but the Germans call it a Thalweg. As can well be imagined this process is very long drawn out and during this time temporary base levels can be caused along the river's path by many things, a lake like Derwentwater, a hard band of rock as we shall see presently, a land-slide or rock-fall. Any such cause may temporarily hold back the water and cause the stream to swing from side to side upstream of the obstruction.

In this way a river along its course may have many phases. For many a mile it may meander across a plain, which it has itself produced, only to enter upon a phase where it is actively cutting down through some obstruction. Here its course will most likely be narrow and its flow rapid.

Crossing the small side stream that here flows into the Derwent, follow the path along its bank to where the ground levels out again and sweeps back to the fell side in a semi-circle. This is an abandoned meander of the river, evidence for which we shall see shortly. Follow the pellucid stream to where the water flows between rocky walls some fifteen feet apart. The river flows more quickly here and it is easy to see that in times of flood the water was at one time very much held back. During some such period it long ago altered its course and cut out the semi-circular path; the pebbles, sand and gravel of its old path are plain enough to see and, after very heavy rain, pools along the path tend to appear. As you continue your walk look out for further meanders of this kind. One of them further upstream is still partly filled with water and is in fact an "ox-bow lake" on a small scale, slowly filling up. From here further progress seems to be blocked by a steep rock which drops down sheer into the water but, by bearing to the right, you can easily mount a step-like rock face to find yourself on top. Before you, sloping steeply down almost to river level, but at right angles to it, is a beautifully smoothed rock face of great extent, a truly magnificent roche moutonnée.

Glaciers are often spoken of as "rivers of ice" but this analogy needs many reservations. For one thing ice, unlike water, will cheerfully run uphill driven by the pressure of the snowfield above, and this it often does when it meets an obstruction such as the one upon which we are now standing. In doing so it smoothes and polishes the surface and then settles down on the valley floor below the obstruction. Here again, unlike water, it may rest long enough to freeze firmly to the rock, and when next it moves it plucks away the downstream side of the rock to leave a steep rough surface like the one up which you have just scrambled. I think that now you might follow the river to Rosthwaite and see for yourself what river features you can see and interpret.

From Rosthwaite follow the main road towards Keswick until you come to a place where there is a raised footpath by the side of the road and white flood posts marked in feet and inches. Looking around you will see that the fields on either side are noticeably flat; the site of an old lake of not so long ago. This sheet of water was held up by the choking of the Jaws of Borrowdale by glacial drift. Not until the river had swept this away could the lake be drained. In its later stages this process would be very slow for the river, as we have seen, had come down to solid rock. It is because the gorge still acts as a bottleneck that the land hereabouts floods under heavy rain, but I suspect that man, in the shape of the River Board, has taken a hand in the matter in more recent years.

Continue to where the road rises up Red Brow and here on the right, a roche moutonnée has been truncated in road widening operations. Above is a bank of typical glacial drift which is worth a little examination. Notice first that the stones embedded in the clay are of all shapes and sizes. A river tends to sort the material it carries, but ice does not. Rivers also tend to lay down their burden in layers, but not so ice. Hence banks of clay like this can generally be put down to the work of ice. In this case there can be little doubt as the clay stands on a fine striated roche moutonnée. Even where this is not the case a little searching among the embedded stones usually produces one or two showing deep cut stria along their length, where they have been dragged across a rocky floor while frozen into the sole of the glacier.

Round the bend in the road is a lovely vista down the Derwent which we have seen before from the opposite bank. I want you now, however, to watch the walls of the steep cutting along the right of the road. Here beds of volcanics have been exposed standing up on end. Some of the beds are dark andesitic lavas and contain many variously shaped splotches. some light coloured. some dark. These are the amygdales we discussed in Cat Ghyll. "Amygdale" refers to almonds and often on examination they turn out to have this shape, although this is more marked in some other lavas—the Derbyshire "toadstones" for instance. All lavas. as was mentioned, contain water, often in chemical combination with other elements. With any relief in pressure some of this water will leave the crystal lattice and flash into steam, the expansion of which causes little vesicles. As the lava is still flowing, the originally round holes tend to become almond shaped. Later these vesicles tend to be filled with minerals deposited from solution, as we see here. In more basic lavas, like the toadstones, these infillings are often very beautiful indeed. Referred to collectively as "zeolites" they are complex aluminium silicates but here the filling is more usually calcite, or some form of quartz, while the darker ones are chlorite.

From here to the Bowder Stone is not far. The stone itself is a huge block perched precariously on end. There has been much argument as to how it comes to occupy its present position. It is said to have fallen from the cliffs above, or it was left by the ice as it melted. The second explanation seems the more likely to me. Coming to rest supported by ice would allow the block to settle quietly down, and it must be remembered that while the size of a block a river can move depends on its rate of flow, a river of ice knows no such limitations!

Still following the road to Keswick you will come to a quarry and the entrance to a newly made car park. This is the old Rainspot Slate Quarry. It has not worked now for many years but I think you will have no difficulty finding specimens from the tips. Much of the stuff is plain green slate, a cleaved volcanic ash, but some you can still find will have darker splotches in it. This is the so-called Rainspot Slate, and the darker markings are due to angular pieces of volcanic material blown from the vent along with the finer ash.

From here it is a pleasant walk to Lodore. If you still have time and energy before you take boat or bus you might wish to visit the falls. A fine example of how water descends from a hanging valley to the main valley, only after heavy rain are they likely to excite the visitor, but there is a geological reason for making the visit. See if you can work it out for yourself. I will only hint that the rock which bounds the falls and the rock over which you make your approach is quite different.

7.   The Skiddaw Granite

MAKE your way to the village of Threlkeld. Follow the steep road up the slopes of Blencathra to the Sanatorium. Just before you reach the entrance gates turn and face south across the valley. In the west Blaeberry Fell stands high above Derwent-water, whilst the Vale of Naddle lies to the east. The ridge of Low and High Rigg divides this dale from the Vale of St. John, with the Helvellyn range rising straight in front of you. A close inspection of this sweep of country shows the slope of the beds of the Volcanics from west to east to be quite noticeable. This slope is what the geologist calls "dip", and it is the angle made by the beds with the horizontal.

Now look at the end of the Helvellyn range where it is gashed by the Threlkeld Granite quarries. Above the quarries the fell side shows a quite perceptible dome. This doming is interesting because the Threlkeld Micro-granite is younger than the Borrow-dales and Skiddaw Slates and was pushed up into them, arching the beds in the process. This kind of intrusion is known as a Laccolith. While all the granites of the Lake District were, at one time, thought to have this form, the one you are looking at now seems to be the best authenticated.

After passing the entrance gate to the Sanatorium, and the gate across the road, you will find a small quarry on the fell side. Here you can see Skiddaw Slate overlain by Glacial Drift. Many boulders are lying about, and most of these you will readily recognise as originating from the Borrowdale Volcanics. They do not belong here for, as you can see, the fell side is composed of Skiddaw Slate. They are "erratics"—stones carried by the ice on to rocks of a different character, rocks to which they quite often bear no relationship. As most of the Volcanics crop out to the south on the other side of the valley, we have here an example of the complicated pattern woven by the ice in Glacial times. A glacier coming down from the Vale of St. John met other ice and was pushed up here on to the fell side before being forced eastwards towards Penrith. On melting it dropped its burden here for you to find. Although much work has been done on the Ice Age in these parts it is not always easy to unravel all the movements of even the last of the onsets.

From here follow the rough road round the fell until you stand looking at the shoulder of Skiddaw known as Lonscale Fell. At your feet, running almost north and south, is the Glenderaterra valley, with its grand old British name. The valley follows a line of fault which continues down the Vale of St. John, through Thirlmere, over Dunmail Raise down through Grasmere and Rydal, and along the length of Windermere. It is one of the "shatter belts" described by Professor Marr. Erosion over millions of years has found and exploited the line of weakness. Whether, at our feet, the rocks are shattered to the extent visualised by Marr is a moot point for there is little to see except the long valley trough. But there are other shatter belts, some of which run east and west, like the one that runs up Langdale and over Esk Hause by Sprinkling Tarn, across Styhead and up between the Gables to run down Ennerdale. This belt, at least where it crosses the mountains, is well defined, and the broken rock can be seen in many places between Rosset Ghyll and Styhead Tarn, and again in Aaron's Slack between Great and Green Gable. This shatter belt has not only been exploited by the weather, but at some time long ago by mineral bearing solutions carrying haematite. As a result the shattered rock is predominantly red.

Let us continue along the rough track, avoiding the one that goes down to the valley floor and the old Glenderaterra Mine and following the upper one to where it makes a sharp bend into the fell side. Here a small stream flows under the road. Stop at this point (Grid Ref. 299270) and examine the rocks cropping out in the bank by the stream and you will find a dark grey mudstone shot through with long straight white crystals. Where the crystals are broken across they have a perfectly square cross-section, often with a black dot in the middle. These are crystals of chiastolite and they are a secondary phenomena having been produced in situ by the heat given off by the nearby Skiddaw Granite. This granite found its way into the anticline (or dome) when the slates were folded in Caledonian times. Although, as yet, not much granite is to be seen, the fact that the slates have been altered by heat over an area of some 30 square miles suggests that the granite is not very far below the surface over a wide area.

This altering of rocks, and the producing of new minerals in them due to heat, is known as "metamorphism", literally a change of form. Let us look a little further into what has happened here. Our Skiddaw Slates were built up from beds of mud and sandy mud (or silt) laid down on the sea floor many millions of years ago. Much of this material was of a clay nature with, in the case of silt, fine grains of sand (quartz) and in both cases probably a good deal of a mineral called mica. All clays—and there are many different kinds—have one thing in common; they are, like the micas, complex aluminium silicates with water as a member of the crystal lattice. When heat is applied water is driven off and the aluminium silicates re-arrange themselves to give a denser more closely-packed crystal lattice. The new minerals are therefore harder and heavier than the clays and micas from which they came. Such changes are usual around any deep-seated igneous mass but are more pronounced around granite masses than intrusions of a more basic character. Before leaving here notice that on the wall of the ghyll below the path the rocks are reddened by haematite which has found its way up a small fault. I have found small specimens of "kidney ore" here.

Continue along the track to where it crosses a larger stream. This is Roughtenghyll. Notice the flagstones that were used to span the stream. The flags are composed of a hard, tough rock with tiny dark spots, the "spotted slates" of the older geologists. Hit with a hammer they emit a musical ring, and this is the source of the famous "Skiddaw Musical Stones", a fine collection of which, in the form of a xylophone, can be seen in the Keswick Museum. The hardening and spotting is again due to heat but the rocks were originally sandy mudstones or silts, not mudstones. The spots are thought to be caused by concentrations of iron sulphide which have migrated due to heat.

The next stream, Sinen Ghyll, is the one we want, so leave the track and follow the stream up. You will notice that after a time patches of white gravel begin to appear in the pools (most have now been swept away by the stream), and as you continue upstream the amount of gravel increases. The white gravel is mostly felspar from the granite and in following this clue you are imitating the prospector when he seeks for gold. Possibly, like us, he would find his vein making a waterfall as the Skiddaw Granite does here. If you knock off a piece of the rock over which the water falls you may then examine it closely with a lens. Probably the first things you will notice will be comparatively large white crystals. These are felspars. Other, much smaller pieces, are either a glittering bronze or else black, and these are flakes of mica. Between the two you will find irregular shaped bits of a glassy-looking material which is quartz. Most granites are characterised by these three constituents, and while the colour of the felspar varies, as does the colour of the micas, you should now be able to recognise this class of rock when you see it. Many granites are very lovely rocks. They take a good polish, and are much used for decorative purposes, one result of this being that although you live in a large town or city you can derive much fun from studying shop front, banks or even the local graveyard!

The detailed study of rocks is almost a science in itself. It is certainly a special branch of geology known as Petrology and much can be learned from such a study. The expert takes his rock and cuts from it a thin slice. Carefully polishing one face to remove, so far as possible, all scratches, he cements the polished face of the specimen to a glass slide. With great patience he will then rub down his section until it is so thin he can see light through it. It is now ready for examination under a special kind of microscope. Probably he will have to continue his rubbing (very carefully) until he gets just the right thickness. To do this, entirely by hand, as was first done by Professor Sorby of Sheffield many years ago, is a very slow and laborious process. The slide prepared, what can be seen? And what does it tell us?

Under the microscope our rock is seen to be made up of definite crystals, and bits of crystals, in a glassy matrix. The smaller crystals are dark and when well developed are hexagonal in shape. These are micas, and as they often seem to be enclosed in the white felspars, as well as in the glassy quartz, it looks as if they grew first. When we turn our attention to the felspars we find that they often show a layered structure, rather like the skins of an onion. Some show a definite lath shape with pointed ends, and these are fully developed crystals. They must have had plenty of room in which to grow. Between the crystals is the quartz with no definite shape at all.

Although it has no shape it is not without interest for it often contains tiny cavities. In some of these cavities can be seen small bubbles which move as the slide is turned. It looks as if the cavities contain a liquid, as indeed they do. Careful examination of the mica crystals in many granites show, enclosed within them, very small colourless needles. The mica crystals seem to have grown round them just as the felspars have enclosed the micas. This then is what the petrologist can see on his carefully prepared slide. What does it tell us? Our rock is composed mostly of crystals that have grown from a mother liquor and grown in a very definite sequence.

Of what was this mother liquor composed? This question can be answered by making careful chemical analyses of granite rocks. The average composition of granites from all over the world runs something like this:

SiO_2	70.18%	TiO_2	0.39%
Al_2O_3	14.47%	Fe_2O_3	1.57%
FeO	1.78%	MnO	0.12%
MgO	0.88%	CaO	1.99%
Na_2O	3.48%	K_2O	4.11%
H_2O	0.84%	P_2O_5	0.19%

From this it appears that our original mixture was highly complex, with silica and alumina predominating but a lot of other elements present in small amounts. Zirconium is present in such small amounts as not to come out in this average analysis of some 500 different granites. To make such a mixture liquid requires quite a high temperature, so our granite evidently starts off deep down within the earth's crust where such temperatures are to be found. Once our melt found its way nearer to the surface, as it did here in the base of the Skiddaw Anticline, it would slowly begin to cool and the complex sequence of crystallization of different minerals commence, the end point of which we have here in our hand, the Skiddaw Granite.

In the granites where zirconium is present we suspect that the tiny needle-like laths of zircon grow first. So we have a picture of zirconium atoms moving about in our cooling liquor until they meet and unite with atoms of silicon and oxygen. Nuclei once formed would grow into tiny crystals until all the zirconium was used up when this first stage of the process would stop, giving us tiny zircons floating about in the mother liquor. As the temperature continued to fall other groupings of atoms would take place, with the zircons acting as focal points. We have seen that the zircons are usually enclosed in the micas and these are the next crystals to be formed from a complex assortment of atoms which include silicon, aluminium, potassium, oxygen and hydrogen and sometimes iron and magnesium. It is the iron content that gives the micas their dark colour.

As cooling continues felspar nuclei appear. Felspars can be very complex, and their composition greatly depends on the original elemental make-up of the melt. Often they form a graded series with a felspar called albite (sodium aluminium silicate) at one end, to anorthite (calcium aluminium silicate), at the other end of the series. Between these two end points there are varying mixtures in which differing amounts of sodium and calcium are found together. It is the availability of these two elements which gives rise to the layered structure of many felspars. Often the core of a crystal will be a pure lime felspar, but as calcium becomes scarcer some of it will be replaced by sodium until finally the outer skin of the crystal will consist of pure soda felspar, or albite. While these plagioclase felspars (as they are called) are forming, should there be any potassium left over from the forming of mica, a different kind of felspar will be formed called orthoclase, a potassium aluminium silicate.

Still left in the melt will be all the silicon which could not be absorbed in the making of the silicate crystals, plus the metallic elements, plus active gases and probably super-heated water. At this stage silicon picks up oxygen to form silica, or quartz, but as most of the space is already occupied by previously formed crystals all the quartz can do is to fit in to whatever spaces it can find. As the quartz consolidates it often encloses tiny bubbles of gas which give rise to the cavities already noted. But also during this process it, along with the rest of the mass, shrinks as the temperature falls and so exerts a high pressure on the gas. Under this great pressure the gas, which is mostly carbon dioxide, liquefies, and so we have the appearance of bubbles in the liquid-filled cavity. From the relationship between the amount of carbon dioxide in liquid form and the size of the cavity, it is possible to work out the temperature at which the residual quartz finally solidifies; it turns out to be about 700 degrees centigrade.

Much has been learned about these complex reactions by studying silicate melts in the laboratory. It is possible to get the temperatures required, but more difficult is the task of applying *The Skiddaw Granite* 49 anything like the requisite pressures. Another point which should not be overlooked is the time factor. A man's lifetime is as nothing compared with the time taken for a granite mass to freeze under a cover of thousands of feet of solid rock, as the Skiddaw Granite probably did here.

Above the fall, floods of recent years have brought about many changes. More granite is exposed than previously and in the northern bank there is now a most interesting exposure. The granite here is very fine grained and is overlain by a band of white quartz, while up the bank the baked Skiddaw Grit is seen in contact. In this exposure we are looking at the actual roof of the granite, leaving no doubt that in this case we are dealing with a granite intrusion in the old sense, rather than with granitisation. The rock overlying the granite is sometimes called a mica schist or, alternatively, a cordierite hornsfels. Perhaps the latter is the better name; on a fresh break glistening bits of mica can be seen but petrological examination shows both cordierite and odd garnets. The absence of kyanite and sillimanite suggests low temperature intrusion.

Going back to the ghyll below the granite, follow the south bank for a little way downstream and in a high bank you will find a white looking exposure. This is the real source of the bits of felspar you found in the stream and a little search should provide quite sizeable pieces from the soft clayey mass. This exposure is worth close examination. It shows how a seemingly hard rock like granite can disintegrate and be swept away by the action of the weather. Water-carrying carbonic acid from the atmosphere, and peaty acids from the soil, attack the big white felspars and break them down. Felspars are either potassium, or calcium, or sodium aluminium silicates and they break down in this way:

$$Al_2Si_2O_5(OH)_4 \quad (Clay\ minerals)$$
$$6H_2O + CO_2 + 2K.AL.Si_8O_8 = 4SiO_2 4H_2O \quad (Silicic\ Acid)$$
$$K_2CO_3 \quad (Removed\ in\ Solution)$$

The potassium carbonate is carried away in solution to become the food of plants. The $Al_2Si_2O_5(OH)_4$ group is mostly china clay, and although a little of the silica goes into solution as silicic acid most of the rest provides the quartz grains for sand. The clays go to form the raw material of our shales and mudstones, the sand provides for our sandstones. All granites suffer erosion in this way and it was thought at one time that this was how the famous china clay deposits of Cornwall had ben formed. When it was found that the clay went down and down, far below the reach of the weather, some other explanation was required. It has been mentioned that in the closing stages of the cooling of a granite mass, hot gases and fluids are given off. It is these emanations that are responsible for mineralization, but quite often they also attack the granite itself. Sometimes the felspars are changed into tourmaline, but more often they become china clay. When I first saw this exposure, many years ago, I wondered if something of that sort had happened here, if only on a small scale. Now that time has increased the exposure I think we can accept the peaty acids percolating down as responsible.

Leaving this interesting exposure let us return down Sinen Ghyll to where it joins the Glenderaterra. Here in the angle made by Sinen Ghyll and the main stream you may see, exposed in the bank, small veins carrying copper. A little search should show you chalcopyrites, the primary ore of copper, a brassy-looking material that tarnishes to browns and purple. Here, too, I have found malachite and azurite. Both are carbonates of copper. The first is a brilliant green and the second a sky blue. The marked difference in colour is not easy to account for, it hardly seems a sufficient explanation that azurite contains slightly more water of crystallization than does malachite. Little is as yet known about the cause of colour in minerals.

A little further down the valley you can visit the tips of the old Glenderaterra Mine which last worked about 1920 and produced mainly lead. On the tips specimens of Galena and Sphalerite can be found. Pyromorphite (Green Lead Ore) can be found too, though the specimens are usually small. Somewhat sparingly the long white needles of Cerussite occur in vugs. From here you can follow the old mine road back to Threlkeld.

8.   Shap Granite and its Surroundings

ABOUT two miles S.S.W. of Shap summit, and just above the bleak A6 road stands Wasdale Crag. It is the source of the now world-famous Shap Granite. At one time you could have gone up the entrance road and into the quarry and no one would have bothered very much. Both management and men were well accustomed to hammer-carrying visitors. Unfortunately, some years ago, the quarry was raided by safe-breakers who broke into the explosives store and made off with large quantities of explosives and detonators. This led to considerable tightening up by both police and the quarry people, so that now it is advisable either to write beforehand or at once to contact someone in authority on the spot. Permission is rarely refused to people who are interested. Courtesy not only pays but, I like to think, is a characteristic of all good geologists.

Having arrived on the quarry floor, what can be seen?

About half of the huge quarry face will be clear, perhaps with men putting in tunnels ready for the next blast. The other half will have at its foot a quantity of rock (the amount depending on how long it is since the last blast) in blocks of all sizes. If you pick up a piece of the rock and examine it you will at once be struck by the large flesh-coloured felspars, while between these you will be able to pick out the black mica and the glassy quartz. Your specimen may be a light grey in colour or much darker, almost a red, for there are two varieties, "light" and "dark". The magnificent felspars are mixed, some being orthoclase and some plagioclase. This is a good place to try and spot the difference. If you turn a specimen from side to side in the light and watch a particular felspar crystal you will soon notice that the light is reflected differently along its length. Some crystals seem to be divided into two down their length and these are orthoclase. Others have not one line of division but many, and these are the plagioclase felspars which are not quite so easy to spot as the orthoclase.

Strictly speaking, Shap Granite is not a granite at all, and those of you who have seen the Skiddaw Granite will already have noticed that it is quite different in appearance. The Shap felspars are very large and are known as "porphyritic". Such felspars are not characteristic of granites as a class. The chemical composition of this rock from Shap does not fit it quite for the true granite class either, and technically it is known as an adamellite.

The exposure of the granite (for despite its technical name it is always spoken of as a granite) is oval in shape, being about two miles from east to west by just short of a mile from north to south. Wherever contacts can be seen, the granite is against Palaeozoics, either Ordovician or Silurian, but to this point we will come back later. Meanwhile if you want to collect specimens you will need the two types, light and dark. While you are looking for these keep your eyes open for what the quarrymen call "heathens". These dark patches in the lighter granite are not always easy to find and you may need the assistance of the quarrymen, particularly if you want one small enough to take away. These patches are generally of a greenish grey colour and often contain odd crystals of felspar dotted about. The crystals are mostly of a dark hue, almost red, but around the edge there is a rim of lighter hue. They are known as re-action rims and are due to the interaction between the acid felspars and their more basic surroundings.

The origin of these heathens has given rise to much discussion. Professor Marr believed that the molten magma from which the granite originated had two phases; an acid one and a more basic one. The more basic one was injected first and the acid one later. The heathens are simply clots of this more basic material taken up in the later granite. Most of the more basic material has found its way into dykes which radiate around the granite and in these rocks you often find isolated crystals of felspar just as you do in the heathen. This is certainly true, one good example being in Swindale Beck near Knock, in the Cross Fell area. On the other hand, the heathen may be bits of the old roof into which the granite was emplaced. Pieces of roof material broken off by what is now referred to as "magmatic stoping" would tend to sink into the molten mass because solid rock is denser than molten rock. Much of this material would be completely absorbed to become part of the melt and all trace be lost.

The great objection to this theory is the presence of the felspar crystals. "How", it is asked, "could felspars possibly grow in the midst of solid rock?" It is a fair enough question, and one to which we have no entirely satisfactory answer. What is well-known today is that they do, and this has been found in many parts of the world. It may be pointed out that the granite is not very acid. With a silica percentage of around 68, it is less acid than the average granite. This may be due to the absorption of much roof material.

Leaving this thorny argument to the experts, what else is there to see? You may remember that granites are usually well jointed and this is easy enough to see here. The faces of these joints, more particularly the perpendicular ones, are worthy of attention, and especially towards the northern end of the quarry, where they often carry minerals. Perhaps the commonest mineral to find its way up the joints is iron pyrites. Of a pale yellow colour it has so often been mistaken for gold that it is sometimes called "fools gold". It is far too hard for the precious metal. You may find a bluey-grey mineral in rather soft scales; and this is molybdenite. Along with it there is a steely-grey mineral, much harder than molybdenite and more plate-like in appearance, which is bismuthinite. Cast around for "vugs", holes in the granite. They are not uncommon and are often lined with crystals of felspar, both orthoclase and plagioclase. Sometimes along with them you may spot more colourful crystals, which may be either a pale lilac or a pale green. These are crystals of fluor, rather peculiar crystals of fluor at that, for while most fluor spar crystals are perfect cubes these are more often cubes with the corners missing. If you have no luck at this it may be as well to ask the quarrymen.

When you have seen and collected all you wish, thank the quarry people and make your way back to the A6. A few minutes' walk in the direction of Shap will bring you to the entrance of another quarry, the so called Blue Rock Quarry. Another fine example of the quarryman's art, this is worked in rocks of the Borrowdale Volcanic series, but here the lavas and ashes have been so altered by the heat of contact with the Shap Granite as to be almost unrecognisable. What you will find will depend to some extent on which particular part of the quarry is being worked at the time of your visit. The first thing to realise is that these rocks were already of some age, with a well developed jointing system of their own, before the emplacement of the granite. It is in the joints and many faults that one should look for the various minerals that have been found here. Some of these joints and faults have been so invaded as to become small veins.

A pale green mineral, which you may have seen before, is epidote, and associated with this one often finds quite sizeable garnets. Unlike the almadine garnets of the Borrowdales these are dark brown in colour and have a resinous appearance. Garnets are very complex things. All the different varieties are complex aluminium silicates, and it is rare to find what might be called a pure garnet, but these in the Blue Rock Quarry are a mixture of Andradite, Grossularite, Pyrope and Spessartine. Among the minerals that have been recorded from the garnet-bearing veins are quartz, calcite, pyrites, chalcopyrites, galena, zinc blende, molybdenite, magnetite and haematite. Besides the changes brought by heat of contact, it is probable that there was a later invasion of lines of weakness by hydrothermal fluids.

There is one thing of importance to notice. These rocks are of Ordovician age. Since the heat of contact has altered them, the ganite is younger than Ordovician. Not far away on Packhorse Hill there are Silurian grits that have been altered to quartzites, so the granite must also be post-Silurian. Leaving the Blue Rock Quarry let us make our way down to the *Shap Wells Hotel,* a little way off the main A6 road. Here before the hotel you will notice a steep bank a little way up the stream from the road. At this point you will find the old Palaeozoics (Brathay Flags) up on end, and lying across their weathered edges, a greenish grey conglomerate. This is the basement bed of the Carboniferous, and in it you will find bits of fresh pink felspar from the nearby Shap Granite. Our granite then is younger than the Silurians, which it has altered, but was itself old by Carboniferous times, since by then it was not only consolidated but exposed. Its age can only be Devonian.

I hope you have been able to follow this chain of reasoning and I wish there were other granite masses in Lakeland to which we could apply it, but this is not so. The age of the Shap Granite is the only one of which we can speak with any certainty until someone does some radio-activity determinations on others. N.B. Much work has been done in the last few years on radio-active dating:

Shap Adamellite (Rubidium-Strontium) 397 ± 11 M.Y.
Skiddaw Granite (Rubidium-Strontium) 365 ± 12 M.Y.
Eskdale Granite. Around 385 M.Y.

9.   Seathwaite, Gillercoomb and Honister

SEATHWAITE in Borrowdale stands in a wide U-shaped glacial valley whose floor has to some extent been evened out by the swinging of the infant Derwent. At Stockley Bridge the Grainsghyll comes down from Great End. To the right, Styhead Ghyll tumbles down Taylor Ghyll Force. Both these valleys distinctly overhang in their upper part. Sour Milk Ghyll falls several hundred feet from the magnificent hanging valley of Gillercoomb.

Here we have a fine illustration of the work of snow and ice during the Glacial Period. From the gathering grounds above, ice tongues were pushed down Grainsghyll, Styhead and Gillercoomb and in their passage they widened and deepened their respective valleys. At the head of the Seathwaite valley the ice from Grainsghyll would be added to the Styhead ice. The combined weight and mass of this glacier would enable it to do even more eroding. The ice debouching from Gillercoomb would increase the effect, thus cutting the valley in which you are standing much deeper than its tributary valleys, and leaving at its head what is sometimes graphically described as a "trough end". Study the drawing and I think it will help you to visualise its application to the present case.

Before we climb up to investigate Gillercoomb, having crossed the river behind the farm buildings, bear right up the fell to where some old mine tips can be seen. Avoiding the first tip continue to the second, a little higher and further over to the right. It is often as well in visiting mine tips in search of specimens to remember that man is a proverbially lazy animal; he always goes for the easiest! So it has been here, and as a result finding anything on the first tip is well nigh impossible. On the second tip you should pick up, fairly easily, pieces of a dark-coloured rock carrying fragments of a soft lead-like substance. The rock is a diorite, the mineral is the celebrated blacklead or plumbago. It was discovered several hundred years ago at the foot of a tree after a storm and was used for years for marking sheep. Then its uses became extended to such things as casting shot, making moulds, blueing gun barrels and not least as a physic for curing "all manner and maks o' ills" and people came to the dale (or more likely to Keswick) to smuggle the substance out to even as far afield as the continent. The mining of black-lead became so important that George II built guard houses for the protection of the mines; the tumble-down remains of one of these you can still see. Much later this valuable deposit became

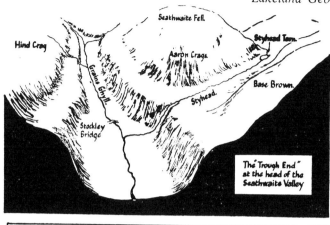

The "Trough End" at the head of the Seathwaite Valley

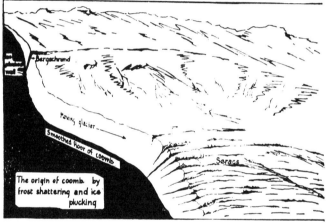

The origin of coomb. by frost shattering and ice plucking

the foundation on which was built the Keswick pencil industry. But what is it? And where did it come from?

Plumbago is one of the natural forms of carbon. It is the apparently amorphous form, the more obviously crystalline form being diamond, and the only difference is the way in which the crystal lattice is built up, for chemically, diamond and graphite are the same. The source of the mineral has long been a cause for argument, but the consensus of opinion seems to favour the Skiddaw Slates. Away back in Ordovician times, some five hundred million years ago, the seas swarmed with minute forms of life much of which was too fragile to leave any impression on the rocks. These tiny forms had one thing in common with the bigger, stouter graptolites and trilobites; they were **living** and so were composed of complex molecules invariably containing carbon. The dead remains of this multitudinous life, showering down into the slowly accumulating mud, raised the carbon content until the general colour of the sediments became dark grey to black. Long after these sediments became rock, heated material was intruded to consolidate as the Eskdale Granite and the heat of the intrusion vaporised and drove off the carbon to condense and form this interesting and world-famous deposit.

You may think that Eskdale is rather a long way off, but an outcrop of this very widespread granite has been mapped around the head of Wasdale hardly more than a mile and a half away. That the geology of the mine is far from simple you soon discern for yourself. Even a cursory examination of the mine tips will disclose a remarkably varied assembly of rock types, in which fault breccia is well represented. It would be interesting to speculate as to why we have plumbago and not diamond but the origin of diamond itself is still a bit of a mystery. It is usually held that besides a high temperature, a high pressure is required for the formation of diamond. Was the overlying cover not thick enough to provide the pressure, or had the pressure been relieved by the intrusion of the diorite? It is just one of the many questions we shall probably never be able to answer.

Leaving the site of these old mines make your way across to Sour Milk Ghyll and climb to where the stream cuts its way through solid rock on leaving the coomb. If you knock off a bit of this hard grey-green stone and examine it carefully you will find it to be composed of fragments, often angular, some large, dark, and set in a finer grained matrix. This is the Harrath Tuff of earlier workers and takes us back to a time when our local volcano was in an explosive phase, covering the area for miles around with showers of fragments and fine glassy dust. This has consolidated to give us the hard tough rock over which the stream now plunges. This episode was somewhat late in volcanic times, for most of the fragments are rhyolitic in character; it may mark the onset of the change from andesite to rhyolite, as can be seen up on Base Brown.

This change of phase is one of the interesting things about volcanic phenomena. Often an eruptive episode will be followed by the extrusion of basic lavas like basalt, but if the episode is long-continued the character of the material tends to change. It becomes, on the whole, less basic and may end up acid. The terms "acid" and "basic" in this context refer to the chemical composition. All igneous rocks are complex mixtures of minerals, the minerals themselves often being compounds in which silica acts as an acid, while elements like aluminium, iron and magnesium act as bases. One way of classifying igneous rocks is to ascertain by analysis the silica content. Roughly speaking, any rock with more than 66% silica is classed as acid. Granites and granophyres fall into this class, as do the extrusive rhyolites. Andesites and diorites, having a silica content falling between 55 and 66% are spoken of as intermediate rocks. Rocks which are lower in silica than 55% are spoken of as basic and in this class fall the gabbros and basalts, examples of which we shall see later.

Obviously such a classification is of limited value in the field, except that certain physical characteristics are linked to the chemical composition. Acid rocks are usually light in colour, and in weight, while basic rocks tend to be dark and heavy. What confuses the issue is the fact that rocks of identical composition, but consolidating under very different conditions, give rise to rocks that look, and are, quite different. A rock like gabbro consolidates at depth from a magma. If poured out at the surface as a lava, it would produce basalt, or if intruded into other rocks as a sill it might well give you a dolerite! No wonder the poor amateur feels at times that the geologist himself doesn't know what he is talking about! What one has to recognise is that the subject of the igneous rocks is a difficult one. It cannot, like many other geological problems, be satisfactorily tackled in a museum or laboratory without reference to what happens in the field, and to recognise this will at least save us, both from despair and the temptation to be too dogmatic!

Let us now go on to the floor of the coomb which is quite extensive. It is still wet and boggy, and the stream tends to meander a little. The ice hemmed in here by the high hills would linger long, and by its long continued plucking action it carved out this fine coomb. Let us take a closer look at the mechanism of coomb formation. As most Alpinists know, as one leaves the snowfield to face the stiffer ascent one is usually confronted by what can be a sinister obstacle in the form of a deep crevasse, the bergschrund, and this has a profound geological significance.

In discussing the onset of the ice age it was noted that before a glacier or an icefield can form, more snow must fall in the winter than the heat of summer can melt, and such conditions would last longest in the fells in locations that had a northerly or north-easterly aspect. It is in such situations that we can look for some of our really fine coombs, like the one in which we are now standing. The heavy snows of winter, by alternately freezing and melting in the summer and by pressure, slowly change from snow to ice and this freezes to the rock face. But the lower glacier itself is slowly melting away and is on the move under the pressure of the snowfield above. The bergschrund appears where the wall of snow and ice gets left behind. In time the sheer weight of unsupported snow and ice becomes too great and it slips down and carries with it masses of rock from the wall behind to which it was frozen. The schrund is in this way closed, fresh snow falls, the ice moves slowly forward once more to open a fresh bergschrund and the repetition of this process over thousands of years has given us our coombs, or as the Scots call them, corries.

When the ice finally melted and retreated up the coomb it left the hummocky moraines you can see in its upper reaches. In all probability there was once a small tarn which could not be drained until the stream had cut its way down to the Tuffs. You can follow the exposure of the Harrath Tuffs for a considerable way along the south-eastern wall of the coomb until its gets lost under a mass of scree. At this point the tuff band is shifted by a fault to reappear on the opposite wall of the coomb. On the floor, but not easy to find, is an outcrop of dolerite very similar to the rock at Castlehead; its age, however, is somewhat doubtful. Climbing up the steep slope on the north-west the outcrop of tuff gets progressively thinner until it dies out altogether. The rock that we next encounter is a lava, the Wrenghyll Andesite; it is a tough rock and in places beautifully flow brecciated. It takes its name from a lakeland locality and from the far away Andes where lavas of this type were first studied.

From the head of Gillercoomb, with marvellous views on every hand, make your way by Brandeth and Grey Knotts towards the old tram track above Honister Hause. If you have plenty of time notice the exposures of Borrowdale Volcanics as you go along. For the most part they are lava flows and you will probably see some which have a red rusty appearance. This weathered look has given rise to the argument that these particular lavas were sub-aerial and not submarine, but not all workers will agree with this. Descending by the old tram track you will come down at the works of the Honister Slate quarries. The quarries, which formerly were mostly great tunnels or caves in the fell side, followed the highly cleaved bands in the Middle Tuffs. There has been a change of practice and the slate is worked opencast on the fell above. The slates are a pleasant green colour and are of great durability; they are also free from the little cubes of iron pyrites so detrimental to some other slates.

If you show interest, the quarry people are usually pleased to show you the whole process of slate making, and this will give you plenty of opportunity to examine the slates themselves. Slates which clearly show bands of deposition are quite common, for this band of the Middle Tuff, some three hundred feet thick, represents a time when volcanic material was exposed above the sea to the weather, and much of the fine detritus was simply washed into place. Sometimes you can find a band of coarser, more angular material representing a fresh eruption. Later the whole mass was crushed and cleaved, and of course faulted, and a little search usually turns out a specimen showing lovely faults on a small enough scale to carry away.

10.   Carrock Fell Area

THE Carrock Fell area is geologically one of our most fascinating. For long its remoteness kept it in splendid isolation; ordinary tourists rarely visited it and it was best known to anglers and to geologists. Scientific interest apart, its rugged wildness makes it worthy of attention and in these days of easy transport I notice it is becoming more popular. Dealing with it as a subject of geology is not easy. There is so much to see in so many different places. Turn off the main road from Threlkeld to Penrith at the signpost that points to Mungrisdale and Heskett Newmarket. On your left is Souther Fell, a shoulder of Blencathra, rising abruptly across a low undulating glacial plain cut by a post-glacial stream. This undulating type of country is usually glacial in origin and it is very marked hereabouts. Souther Fell is carved from Skiddaw Slates, while on the right is the low ridge of Eycott Hill, composed of Borrowdale Volcanics and overlain by Carboniferous Limestone which sweeps eastward, bed above gently sloping bed, until it is itself overlain by the red desert rocks of the Permo-Triassic of Penrith. Looking back along the approach road you see the rounded outline of Great Mell Fell, made up of rock fragments swept from the Devonian deserts.

Passing through the hamlet of Mungrisdale the road twists and twines on its way to Bowscale. As you leave Mungrisdale, behind some new houses, there is an old quarry showing Skiddaw Slates up on end (Grid Ref. 363405). Here the slates have little cleavage, and graptolites, usually Didymograptids, have been found. They take some finding. Walking the road to Bowscale we have the marked contrast of steep fell side on the left, with the Slates peeping out here and there, and on the right an expanse of flat boggy land. This is an obvious lake bed, and it has been filled in since glacial times. Pass through the hamlet of Bowscale and on to Mosedale where a shoulder of Carrock rises behind the cottages marked on the six inch map as "Snailshell Crag". At the foot of this crag, a little way along the Heskett road, is a small quarry which is well worth examining.

Lumps of rock of a pale green colour can be seen on the face parallel with the road. They are surrounded by a fine grained rock which varies from grey to green. The pale green lumps are pieces of Borrowdale Lava of the Eycott Hill group which have been picked up and in part absorbed by the gabbro. On a wall on the right is a contact variety of the gabbro. A little further over, and round the corner, you will find a very dark rock which, hefted in the hand, is noticeably heavy. This is a marginal form of the gabbro, the dark colour and weight being due to minerals rich in iron. Magnetite, a magnetic iron ore, occurs in black shining grains. Grown into the same crystal as the magnetite is the mineral ilmenite, an oxide of titanium. Ilmenite is one of the chief sources of titanium which, after being regarded as useless for long, is now hailed as a wonder metal. It is claimed to be almost as light as aluminium and as tough as steel. If it is alloyed with other metals it can be very resistant to both heat and corrosion, and these are useful properties in the aircraft industry. The magnetite-ilmenite content of the marginal gabbro is around 25—30%, and while it is of no commercial value at the moment, were we ever forced back upon our own resources for titanium it might prove useful.

The igneous rocks of Carrock Fell are usually referred to in geological literature as the "Carrock Fell complex" and this description has been bestowed because of the many different types of rock to be found here, mostly of an igneous origin. Besides requiring a knowledge of the many rock types there is difficulty in interpreting their inter-relationships. We can hardly touch them all, but let us explore a little further.

Traverse along the fell side in a northerly direction and examine the outcrops. You will notice that the gabbro tends to get lighter in colour and in weight (bulk for bulk). This is because the composition of the rock is gradually changing. The magnetite-ilmenite content is getting less and the proportion of big white felspars greater and in this type it is easier to make out the different constituents. First notice the felspars. In these the element sodium has replaced potassium to give a plagioclase felspar.

As was mentioned at Shap it is possible to distinguish between orthoclase and plagioclase even in the field providing you have a lens, a good eye, and preferably a little sun. Choose a specimen with a good big felspar and turning it in your hand watch carefully the play of light on the crystal face. If you have got the light in the right direction you should be able to make out a group of parallel lines running down the length of the crystal. These mark phases of change in the structure and the phenomenon is known to petrologists as "lamellar twinning". It is as if thin slices of the felspar had been turned in such a way that each adjacent one was the mirror image of its partner, and this in fact is what it is.

You can explain it, if you like, by saying that one section is right-handed and the other left-handed. The number of ions is the same, their spacing in the crystal lattice is the same but in effect they face opposite ways. This being so they affect light differently and so by careful observation you can pick out the twin planes. To see the effect at its best, of course, you require a petrological microscope and a thin section. In our specimen the specks of magnetite-ilmenite can be seen along with slender laths of a grey-green mineral. This is diallage, a complex magnesium, calcium, iron silicate.

Careful search high up the fell side will show a gabbro comparable with the one you have been examining, except that it contains free quartz and is thus quartz gabbro. There is not much of this rather unusual rock and the exposure is not easy to find. As you continue the traverse of the fell towards Further Ghyll Syke you will notice that the gabbro begins to get darker and heavier again until you are back once more on the marginal variety you saw behind the cottages at Mosedale. If you were to carefully collect samples and check the specific gravity of each, as Harker did many years ago, you should find that they fall into a sequence that runs something like this:

Mosedale, 3.118.....3.0.....2.99.....2.89.....2.88.....2.99.....3.0.....3.2.....Further Ghyll. From the centre of this igneous mass the rock gets heavier and darker towards the margins.

Professor Harker, who first examined the gabbro in detail, suggested that the contact with the surrounding rocks chilled the margins and caused the concentration of the most easily formed crystals around the periphery, leaving the centre of the magma deficient in heavy minerals and concentrating there the lighter with an excess of silica which came out as free quartz. To this process he gave the name "magmatic differentiation" and his paper started off much heated discussion.

The field relations of the gabbro are not simple. To the south it seems to be separated from the Skiddaw Slates by a fault. The slates do show alteration by heat, but it seems more likely that this was due to the granite rather than the gabbro. On the east a fault separates the gabbro from the Borrowdale Volcanics, here represented by the Eycott Lavas. These not only run round to the north of the igneous complex but can be found as remnants on the summit, so evidently in the first place the mass was intruded into the Eycotts, probably at their junction with the Slates.

Since Harker's time physical-chemists have drawn attention to some theoretically serious objections to his views on differentiation and although the argument has now taken in many other deep-seated igneous masses, I do not know that any satisfactory conclusion has as yet been reached. The last person to work on this interesting area was the late Professor Hollingworth, he thought it likely that the differentiation was done deep down in the earth's crust and then the different types of gabbro were emplaced as sheet injections. To me the order of injection seems very remarkable but I think we had better leave the experts to wrangle and go on to what else can be seen.

Look now at the crags to the north of Further Ghyll Syke. Even to the inexpert eye there is a quite obvious difference in appearance. The gabbro fell side that we have just traversed is a tangle of rough blocks and boulders, due to the fact that the rock is well jointed and thus tends to weather out in blocks. Across the Syke there are few such blocks. Instead, a steep crag is subtended by a fine scree slope. This is obviously a quite different material. As you cross the Syke you will find a close grained, warm tinted rock, very different from the gabbro. This rock is a granophyre and belongs to the granite family. It is made up of felspars, a little quartz, flakes of green mica and odd bits of a dark coloured mineral, augite. Microscopically the quartz and the felspars can be seen to grow into one another in a close intergrowth, the distinguishing feature of a granophyre. In hand specimens it varies from pink to grey, is tough and hard, but tends to weather to small pieces and finally to a fine sand.

Return now to the stream in Further Ghyll Syke and here you will find some very queer-looking rocks indeed. Examined closely they give the impression of an intermixture of gabbro and granophyre, and this is what they are. After the intrusion of the gabbro, but while it was still hot, the granophyre was emplaced, and where it was in contact it assimilated some of the gabbro to give these mixtures. That the granophyre followed the gabbro and not vice versa can be seen quite clearly for close examination along the line of the syke will show veins of granophyre penetrating the gabbro. The junction rock is of some interest with its large crystals, some of which can be found one and a half inches long. The rock consists of felspar, augite, hornblende, and some iron ore along with small amounts of accessory minerals.

Much further over on the fell another igneous type occurs. In the old days it was called a diabase but is now generally called a diorite. Of the three rock masses the diorite is considered to be the youngest, but the age of the complex itself is by no means easy to fix. There is some evidence that the rocks surrounding the complex have been affected by post Silurian movements, but the complex itself seems unaffected. This suggests a Devonian age for the igneous rocks of Carrock Fell but they may be much younger than this and are considered so by some geologists.

Further along the road towards Heskett Newmarket you will notice some small mine tips at the foot of the fell. This is the site of the old Carrock End Mine, worked at one time by the owners of the more famous Roughtenghyll. On the tips you may find ores of lead, copper and a heavy white mineral, barytes, or heavy spar. Not far from these tips a road turns off to the right through a farmyard and across the fields to Linewath Bridge. Here, in the bank of the stream above the bridge (Grid Ref.

361343), you can examine the lowest lava exposed of the Eycott Hill series.

The rock is of a dark green colour and shows conspicuously light green felspars, some of them up to a couple of inches in length; this is bytownite. We have met this kind of crystal before at Shap and they are, you may remember, known as "porphyritic" crystals. The rock is known as the bytownite porphyrite. Porphyrite crystals of this kind in a large igneous mass like the Shap granite are one thing, but similar crystals in a lava are another, and are not easy to account for. Usually lavas cool far too quickly to allow time for the growth of large crystals and the explanation put forward is that the magma had already begun to cool and the crystals had already grown in the magma chamber before the molten material was erupted as lava.

Because of its easily identifiable character the rock is very useful as an erratic, it often turns up along the coast of West Cumberland in the glacial drift, and much further afield than that. Further up the brow there are outcrops of other members of the series but the prettiest is to be found on Greenah Crag, just south of Eycott Hill itself, where felspars of the bytownite type are to be seen in a reddish purple base.

Along the crest of the Eycott ridge the Carboniferous Limestone peeps out in many places. It lies unconformably upon the Volcanics but the actual junction is not easy to find. From Greenah Crag it is not far back to the main Penrith-Keswick road.

*   *   *

FROM Mosedale a good road leads for several miles up the Caldew Valley, and by following it you will soon come to the open fell side with its dark green cover of juniper. High up on the fell side to the south you can see the great coomb occupied by Bowscale Tarn, remnant of the ice age. Following the road you may notice many fine specimens of the Carrock Fell granophyre, but do not allow these to puzzle you, as I have seen them puzzle unwary lads of the hammer! Granophyre does not belong here at all, and in a sense these are "erratics", but they are man-made. They were brought here as road material many years ago.

Most people regard the Lake District as a very wet area with a superfluity of water (after all, Manchester has for many years taken its supplies from the Lakes to the tune of millions of gallons a day, and now seeks more!) Nevertheless the eastern and northern fringes of our area are often very short of water and the old mine road, the line of which we are following, was rebuilt in preparation for the building of a dam and reservoir in the valley. So far the scheme has not been carried out.

Along the roadside and in the river bed you can see fine

Friar's Crag, Derwentwater

Green's Flow Breccia (see page 32)

River Derwent above Derwentwater showing a meander with shingle banks and cutting back action (see page 40)

The Skiddaw Granite at Sinen Ghyll (see page 46)

Low angled fault or thrust plane in bed of the stream behind Hollows Farm, Borrowdale, Grid Ref. 247 171 (see page 38)

Folded Skiddaw Grit in the bend of the Caldew (see page 69)

examples of folding, somewhat reminiscent of the rocks we saw near the granite in Sinen Ghyll, so it will not be a difficult inference to make that here too, at no great distance, the granite is to be found. Further along the road rises sharply to a well built bridge crossing a side stream. This is Grainsghyll Beck, and looking up the valley one can see signs of mining on a large scale.

Ignore the mines for the moment and go down to the bed of the Caldew above the confluence of the two streams. Follow the river upstream until you come to a place where it flows over bedrock. Cursory examination will show that this rock is the Skiddaw Granite. It is for the most part well weathered here but this is by far the largest exposure there is. We have now seen two exposures some three miles apart. There is a third small exposure in Blackhazel Beck in a direct line between the Caldew and Sinen Ghyll.

Return now to the bridge across the Grain. Beneath its well constructed foundations you will find a rock, on the Caldew side, rather like the granite but at the same time also rather different. Above the bridge in the bed of the Grain a rock of different character is well exposed. Known locally as "pepper and salt rock" this is a kind of greisen. I say "a kind of greisen" because the typical rock of the name contains topaz, and so far as I know no topaz has ever been found here. However this may be, it brings us to that very interesting phase in the consolidation of a granite when large quantities of highly active gases and fluids are driven off, the phase known as pneumatolysis. The emanations, which can be very complex, actively attack the granite itself near the margins, break down its constituent minerals, more particularly the felspars, and replace them by others. In this case by a silvery form of muscovite mica known as gilberite, so the rock comes to consist almost entirely of quartz and mica. The greisen extends up the bed of the Grain beyond the mines and high up the side of Coomb Height.

Rejoining the road to the mines, notice that a small stream tumbles down the fell side on the right to join the Grain. This is Poddy Ghyll* (where wulfenite has been reported), and high up in this ghyll, beneath a waterfall, a small vein carries a greeny-black mineral crystallizing in long shiny needles. This is tourmaline, a complex boro-silicate of aluminium and iron. A typical pneumatolytic mineral this, for boron compounds occur in the highly active gases given off at this stage. It is also during this stage that mineralization takes place, so let us make our way to the mines and see what can be found.

The only building now standing is the old mine office-cum-blacksmith's shop, and if its usual denizens today are sheep, it has outlived all the other buildings which once housed the

* Grid Ref. 327330

crushing and separating plant. Brandy Ghyll, which gives its
name to the mine, comes tumbling down from the right above
the first tip heaps. The old adits can be seen running up the fell
side on either side of the Grain.

The "old men"—a convenient name to cover much lost history
—seem to have opened a small cross vein hereabouts for lead,
bits of which you can still find lying about nearer to Brandy
Ghyll. Then about 1854 a man called Emmerson put in further
work. Probably in trying to locate the lead vein he discovered
not lead but wolfram, an ore of tungsten. Unfortunately he was
before his time for tungsten had few uses before the advent of
electric lighting and the tungsten filament lamp, or the discovery
that the element could be used to toughen and harden steel for
cutting tools, or for armour plate. By this time the mines had
been long abandoned and our national supplies came for the
most part from overseas.

Early in the 1914-18 War Great Britain found herself cut off
from these overseas supplies, and tungsten for the war effort
became a matter of national urgency. Thoughts turned to our
own sources of supply, and the Survey were asked to check.
They came here to Carrock, so the story goes, and found not only
the tungsten they were looking for but a mine already in being.
The miners were German and the ore was being shipped out
through Hull to Holland and so to Germany. It is an old tale,
whether true or not I am unable to say, but it is true that
throughout the war the government kept an armed guard here
at 'Brandy Ghyll. Their army huts were still here when I first
visited the place.

Possibly Brandy Ghyll is one of the most interesting mines in
the area for the richness and variety of its minerals. Although
most of the best specimens have long since gone let us look
about and see what can be found among the quartz lying on the
bank, both around and below the old crusher for, if you had no
luck at Shap with molybdenite and bismuthinite, a little search
here may give some success. Molybdenite, you may remember,
is a soft silvery mineral in small pliable flakes. Bismuthinite is
harder than molybdenite and while it has a silvery grey colour
it is not so bright as the latter. Like molybdenite, bismuthinite is
a sulphide. Ordinary bismuthinite is not so bright and shiny as
molybdenite, but there is a variety which is mirror bright, this
is joseite, a telluride of bismuth and one of the world's rare
minerals, having only been found previously at San José in Brazil.

Go now to one of the big dumps and look for wolfram. A
black shiny mineral that is surprisingly heavy, it usually takes a
blade-like form in white quartz. If you have no easy success it
may repay digging a little into the tip, for you must remember
that students and collectors have been combing the tips for over

fifty years! With a little digging I have never failed to find specimens.

Wolfram is a tungstate of manganese and iron. The tungstate of calcium, scheelite, also occurs. It is a yellow resinous-looking mineral and like wolfram is easily spotted by its high specific gravity. Very fine crystallized specimens have been found as glassy four-sided pyramids but they are becoming increasingly rare. In fact specimens of scheelite are not so good to find now and this you can put down to the march of science. Since the invention of the portable short wave ultra-violet lamp, enterprising collectors have found it all too easy to come at night and just pick out the scheelite, betrayed by its lovely lilac fluorescence. While you are looking for scheelite keep an eye open for another mineral, apatite. It occurs as pale green prisms on quartz and I have seen them up to an inch in length. A rather complex mineral of pneumatolysis this, for sometimes it is a fluoro-phosphate of calcium, sometimes a chloro-phosphate.

One mineral you are almost sure to find, a hard tin-white mineral when freshly broken, it tarnishes to yellows and browns and often occurs in tabular crystals which show the lines of crystal growth, mispickel, or arsenical pyrites. A sulpharsenide of iron the mineral contains about 45% of arsenic and this brings us to an unsolved mineralogical mystery. In this particular part of the Lake District we have a very high concentration of arsenic. Why it is found hereabouts and nowhere else, no one knows.

I would not wish to raise false hopes, but in the mineral collection of Oxford University I have seen some lovely nuggets of gold and the collector assured me they had been found here! Try your luck by all means, but I must confess that I have never had any. Mr. W. T. Shaw, manager of Force Crag Mine, confirms that gold has been found here. Gold you can hardly mistake for anything else providing you remember the remarks about "fool's gold".

Here at Brandy Ghyll we have an interesting suite of minerals and one which is usually associated with tin, but apart from spectroscopic detection the mineral has never been found. In pneumatolytic veins, such as these undoubtedly are, there is often a natural zoning, both vertically and radially, around the granite source. The question arises: do the veins go down sufficiently deep for this mineral to exist, as yet undiscovered? So far all the working done has been along traditional lines by cutting self-draining adits into the mountainside. A few carefully placed bore-holes here might be interesting.

If you are prepared for some rough fell walking you could, with interest, follow Brandy Ghyll up its steep course. Beneath the waterfall above the mines, but a short distance below it, a small portion of vein is exposed carrying much mispickel and this has

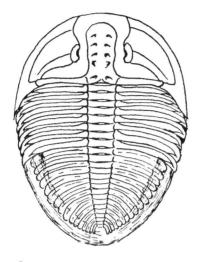

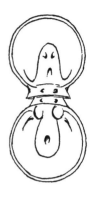

Agnostus sp.

Ogygia buchi.(Brongniart).

Skiddaw Slate Trilobites.
Locality unknown.

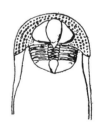

Orthis.   Trinucleus.

Fossils from the Dryghyll Shales

Drawings by H. Shackleton

been altered to a greenish mineral called scorodite, a hydrated ferric arsenate. Above the fall and where the bed of the ghyll widens out a little, notice the steep right-hand wall (facing upstream). To the practised eye an obvious igneous mass is exposed here, and this is one of the things a geologist has to get used to. What a rock looks like when broken across is important but it is also important to notice how any particular kind of rock looks in an exposure. If you cross the stream for a specimen you will find a dark, rather close-grained variety of the gabbro.

In some of the waterfalls, as you ascend the ghyll, you can see traces of the veins exposed, often with small trial holes made by prospectors. In the upper reaches of the stream course are some old tips. For the working of mines here we have no record at all, but the veins cross the Brandy Ghyll veins almost at right angles and on the tips some rather rare and interesting minerals have been found.

On the small tip in the bed of the stream you might look for wulfenite, the rather rare molybdate of lead. It occurs as very small yellow waxy scales, usually on a pale green incrustation. It needs a sharp eye to detect it but I have myself found specimens. On the large tips stolzite, a tungstate of lead can be found as dirty white plates, though they are often iron-stained. On these same tips a vivid green incrustation is fairly common, this is bayldonite, or its near relation, duftite, rather rare and complex lead-copper arsenates. We seem to be in the thick of the arsenic area here, for a chloro-arsenate of lead, mimetite, has been found in lovely, green dusted, hexagonal plates. Not far away in Dryghyll a variant, campylite, can be found.

The suite of minerals here in upper Brandy Ghyll is interesting for it seems to suggest that the roughly east-west lead veins were in existence before the mineralization of the Brandy Ghyll veins with their tungsten, molybdenum and arsenic. *(See footnote, p. 74.)*

It is not very far across to Dryghyll from the head of Brandy Ghyll and the trip is worth making once you are up here. The tips on the floor of Dryghyll (Grid Ref. 322345) are easy enough to spot and a little rooting among them will show plenty of a black carbon-like material. This is a manganese oxide and amongst it one can usually find bits of campylite with the golden yellow, barrel-shaped crystals. The vein which carried the campylite has tumbled in on the brow of the ghyll and can there be seen running through grey shales which have a general dip to the south. The same shales are exposed both above and below the tips in the bed of the ghyll with the same general dip. This is not what one would expect. for the general dip hereabouts is to the north. This can be well seen with the Eycott lavas exposed along Carrock Beck lower down the valley. This suggests complications, and search in the shales will soon confirm this, for fossils are not too difficult to find.

Both fossil shells and trilobites occur and the general fauna would suggest an age about equivalent to that of the Coniston Limestone group. How it comes about that we have this isolated patch of newer rocks perched up here on the fell side entirely surrounded by rocks older than themselves is not easy of explanation. Professor Marr invokes a thrust plane, J. F. N. Green a deep, infold, but possibly they have just been dropped down by faults, of which the campylite vein may be one, and thus preserved. At the moment they are yet another complexity to add to the Carrock Fell Complex. If you want another, can you tell me why on earth anyone should wish to mine camplite? Lead arsenates were not exactly easy to deal with say 100 years ago!

Since the last edition of this book great changes have taken place in the Carrock Fells. The entire mineral rights of the area have been taken over by an American concern and a fine new crushing and sorting plant erected in preparation for the re-opening of the Wolfram Mines. The new owners have asked me to make it quite clear that the mining area is private property and permission to visit should be obtained from World Wide Energy, c/o 43 Station Road, Keswick.

* Recent research has shown the reverse to be the case. The tungsten veins are contemporaneous with the Skiddaw Granite which is roughly 360 M. years old. The E.-W. lead vein is circa 210 M. years. See Moorbath S. 1962. Phil. Trans. of the Royal Society, Vol. 254, pp. 295 et seq.—E.H.S.

11.   The Cockermouth Lavas

COCKERMOUTH is easily accessible from Keswick. Should you follow the main road by Thornthwaite and along Bassenthwaite Lake, and then by the Vale of Embleton, you will be able to see the small "misfit" stream that comes down from Wythop and enters the lake through its reedy bed close by Bassenthwaite station. The Vale of Embleton is the pre-glacial path of the River Derwent, and quite obviously the size of the valley is out of all proportion to the tiny stream that occupies it today. This is due to changes brought about during and at the close of the Glacial Period.

The ice from Borrowdale once swept westwards through the Embleton valley and in its melting left large amounts of drift behind to form a barrier across the valley about Embleton itself. When the ice began to melt many of our valleys were turned into glacier lakes because the water was held up by Irish Sea ice to the west, and the melt waters often found new channels quite different from the once previously followed. The Derwent in this case turned west and cut itself a new channel behind the 800 feet high Elva Hill to flow by Isel, rejoining its old bed near Cockermouth.

Many of the changes brought about during or at the close of the Glacial Period can be spotted if you look carefully at a map of the Lakes, keeping in mind the fact that the drainage was originally radial. Where a river departs markedly from this, such changes can be suspected.

Just before reaching the hamlet of Embleton notice the quarry high up on the fell side on the right of the road. Behind a new petrol station you can still see the remains of a crushing plant. This quarry was worked for road material for many years and was abandoned when, in working down, they came into Skiddaw Slates. The rock being worked was an igneous intrusion of a dioritic type, of a character between a granite and a basalt, and the nature of the intrusion was a flat sheet, or sill. Apart from the quarry, exposures are few, but the tail-end of this sill can be seen at the top of a small quarry at Setmurthy, on the northern side of the fell, where it is intruded into ripple-marked Skiddaw Slates.

The old town of Cockermouth, with its ruined Norman castle, stands where the River Cocker joins the Derwent. As you enter the town by Castle Drive you can hardly fail to notice the new Secondary Modern School, on the terrace of which you can find some very fine erratics, mostly Borrowdale Volcanics, which were dug from the foundations and thoughtfully preserved by our Education Committee.

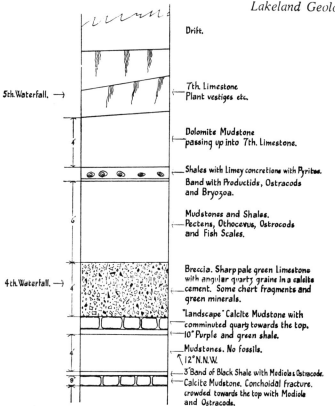

A section in the stream course at Ghyll Wood, Blindcrake, near Cockermouth, drawn by E. H. Shackleton, F.G.S. The diagram is continued opposite

Pass through the town by its tree-lined Main Street. The road to Maryport and Carlisle leaves by a bridge over the Derwent. Follow the main road to Carlisle for about three miles and turn off at the signpost to Redmain (Grid Ref. 136339). Just as you enter the straggling group of houses and farms a lane runs down to the right leading to Park Hill. If you ask, I feel sure the farmer will allow you to proceed to a little tree-crowned knoll just beyond the farm. The rock of this knoll is hard, dark-green in colour, and not easy to break. This is the Cockermouth Lava and examining it carefully you are sure to find small amygdales, usually white, but often stained outside a bright green.

The lava itself is an olivine basalt although, without a microscope, it is doubtful if you will be able to spot the olivine. On weathered surfaces this mineral quickly breaks down but on

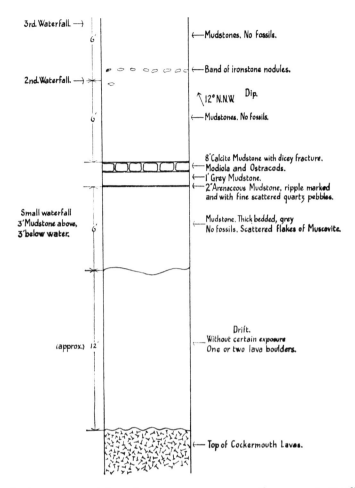

3rd. Waterfall. →

2nd. Waterfall. →

←—Mudstones. No Fossils.

←—Band of ironstone nodules.

↖ 12° N.N.W. Dip.

←—Mudstones. No fossils.

8' Calcite Mudstone with dicey fracture.
←—Modiola and Ostracods.
←—1' Grey Mudstone.
←—2' Arenaceous Mudstone, ripple marked
and with fine scattered quartz pebbles.

Small waterfall
3' Mudstone above,
3' below water.

Mudstone. Thick bedded, grey
No fossils. Scattered flakes of Muscovite.

Drift.
Without certain exposure
One or two lava boulders.

(approx.) 12'

←— Top of Cockermouth Lavas.

fresh fractures, with a lens, you may sometimes spot small crystals of a pale green colour. The lava consists mostly of the mineral augite, with some felspar and a little magnetite, but only in the middle of some of the thicker flows does the rock look at all crystalline to the naked eye. For the most part it is best described, perhaps, by saying it has a stony appearance, cooling having been too quick to allow much crystal growth. Many of the amygdales are of irregular shape, but you do see some that have been drawn out by flow. The middle of a flow is usually free from vesicles or amygdales, mostly they occur at the top of a flow although occasionally at the bottom too. Their presence allows us to distinguish the different flows fairly easily, and to say with some confidence that not all the lava was poured out at the same time. That there is not more drawing out of the amygdales seems to suggest that the flow of the lava was gentle over a fairly level surface.

Roughly 300 feet in thickness, the Cockermouth Lavas consist of four or five distinct flows. That considerable time elapsed between successive flows is shown by the occurrence in a ghyll east of Woodhall of a red bole-like substance between two flows. The first flow had consolidated, and by exposure to the weather had rotted before being covered by the next flow. The redness is due to the prevalence of iron oxides in the lava. Unlike the Borrowdale Lavas there is no evidence that would indicate that these lavas were submarine.

From Park Hill the lavas extend in an easterly direction to Bothel Crags on the Bothel-Keswick road, and in a westerly direction to the village of Brigham on the south side of the Derwent, where they disappear against a fault. Altogether there are more or less continuous exposures for a distance of seven miles.

Originally the lavas were mapped by Clifton Ward as an extension of the Borrowdale Volcanics, with which they are in contact near Binsey to the east. Later, when microscopic examinations came to be made it was realised that the mineral olivine was present. As this mineral does not occur in the Borrowdales nor, so far as is known, anywhere else in Britain in lavas of Borrowdale age, it became evident that further investigation was called for.

Except where faulting intervenes, the basalt forms the high northern bank of the Derwent's course for many a mile, and most of the streams running down this escarpment cut through the lava to reveal some fine exposures. Between the knoll and the farm runs one of these ghylls. If you scramble down into it you will find a very different kind of rock from the basalt. Although the actual junction cannot be seen here, this new rock obviously underlies the basalt. A conglomerate, it is made up entirely of pebbles held together by a sandy calcareous cement. The pebbles themselves are puzzling for, apart from a sandstone which is Skiddavian, few of them can be matched from local rocks exposed today. The general colour of the bed is ruddy and reminiscent of the Mell Fell beds, but for long this conglomerate has been regarded as the basal bed of the Carboniferous.

In this section showing pebble beds overlain by lava, with the lava itself overlain by limestone, which you can see in the fields above the farm, you have a clear illustration of the difficulty sometimes experienced in fixing the age of a formation in the field. The limestones are of undoubtedly Carboniferous age, but in other parts of the Lake country there are Carboniferous limestones much older than these. Underneath the pebble beds you can see in places the Skiddaw Slates, usually up on end; so the Cockermouth Lavas were extruded after Skiddavian times, also after the accumulation of pebble beds of indeterminate age, but before some of the Carboniferous limestone. In both Scotland and Derbyshire there are olivine basalts of undoubted lower Carboniferous age. By analogy the Cockermouth Lavas are assumed to be of this age too, and the pebble beds underneath them were assumed to be the basal beds of the Carboniferous in these parts. There is, however, evidence available which has long lain unobserved, let us go and see this for ourselves.

Going back to the main road (having made sure all our farmer friends' gates are shut) proceed from Redmain to Blindcrake where, at the end of the village, you will find Ghyll Yeat Inn, the ghyll being another ravine that cuts down through the escarpment to join the Derwent. A road runs downhill parallel with the wooded ravine, and about half way between the inn and the bottom of the hill a footpath runs off into woods (cut down, 1965) and dips down to a footbridge. Follow this path to the bridge (Grid Ref. 149341). (Since the wood was cut down both footpath and footbridge have disappeared. The section is now more easily followed in reverse: i.e. Start from the top just below the inn.)

The rocks cropping out in the stream-course below the bridge are basalt. Breaking a piece off you will find a rather puzzling brownish coloured rock, very unlike the basalt you saw at Park Hill. The change is due to weathering and its effect on the rather high iron content. In the bank about 100 yards below the bridge, and on the road side of the stream, you can see the top of one of the lava flows. Upstream from the bridge the stream-course is floored by boulders, but here and there are to be seen obvious outcrops of solid rock. A little tapping will reveal basalt.

Two streams enter, one after the other from the left, and in the second the water falls over a bastion of basalt. On the main stream however, a little way above the confluence, a small water-fall shows shales but even the most careful search has so far produced no fossils. The stream is getting steeper now and a little further up a second fall is caused by a dark hard band of rock. An examination of this rock will show fossil mussels beautifully preserved and what look like black, shiny lentils. The "mussels" are a well-known type to which the name Modiola has been given. The lentil-like remains were once water fleas, or ostracods. The rock in which the fossils are found is a calcite mudstone and consists of fine black mud well cemented with calcium carbonate.

More shales follow as we go upstream, again without fossils. But at the next waterfall, which like the last is caused by a calcite mudstone, we have more numerous modiola and ostracods, though these are crowded together at the top of a nine-inch band. Above this calcite mudstone lies a band of shale some three inches thick and this is crowded with fossils. The shale, being soft, has been swept off the top of the fall by the stream and search must be made for this band in the bank. At the next fall a four-foot band of rock is made up of sharp angular fragments cemented together by calcium carbonate. Above this there are more shales, but these are fossiliferous and contain the remains of shells, bryozoans and other marine creatures. The last fall is of limestone.

How are we to interpret this section? We have first basaltic lava flows, and these are overlain by soft mudstones. A land surface covered by basalt quietly subsided beneath the Carboniferous sea, to be covered in time by mud. The sea deepened and cleared sufficiently for impure limestone (the first calcite mudstone) to be formed and at this time a few modiola and ostracods were struggling to establish themselves. More mud was washed in and the living organisms gave up the struggle until the water cleared again to allow the formation of more calcite mudstone. The modiola and the ostracods returned in force to become so well established that for a time they even survived the return of muddier conditions. Finally they died in swarms, their remains to be preserved in the thin band of mudstones immediately above the fall.

This was followed by a quiet period for mud accumulated for sufficiently long to allow six feet of mudstone to form before the conditions changed. A vigorous current carried in fragments to form the four feet of breccia we find at the next fall. These fragments were carried no great distance from a rapidly weathering land surface, for they are all sharp and angular. Somewhere a limestone was exposed for some of the fragments are of this rock. Most probably it was of Upper Ordovician or Silurian age but no vestige of this remains today any nearer than Shap.

After this episode the water became more truly marine for the overlying shales contain many well-preserved marine shells of the Productus and Spirifer class as well as the remains of cuttlefish-like creatures and fish scales. That conditions of deposition were once more very quiet is demonstrated by the fact that some of the productids still have their spines attached to their shells. Finally the water deepened, or cleared, sufficiently for many hundreds of feet of limestone to be laid down, and this series can be traced over the hill to the north.

The deposits we have examined in this section show all the characteristics of quiet lagoon conditions compatible with the events described. It shows, in my opinion, the true onset of Carboniferous deposits in this area. This leaves us with 300 feet of basalt which, if Carboniferous, must have been extruded in the earlier part of that era. That the period of extrusion was extended we know because some of the flows have weathered surfaces. What then of the pebble beds which underlie the basalts? These, I think, can only be regarded as the sweepings of the old Devonian land surface, and of Devonian age.

If you have had the patience and persistence to follow this section you will have seen something that few people besides myself have seen. That some geologists might differ a little in their interpretation I am willing to agree, but at least you should be able to follow how we try to interpret the riddle of the past from the evidence of the rocks and their contents.

A scramble up the bank will bring you back to the road just below the inn and so in a position to start your return journey. If, however, you have time to spare, a walk eastwards across the fields is worthwhile. Passing through the gate opposite the inn you will soon be rewarded by some fine views of the countryside sweeping right across to Skiddaw. Below you is the deep cut valley of the Derwent, cut since glacial times. Notice how, by swinging from side to side, it has widened its trench and now meanders. The width of the valley is due mostly to the swollen melt waters as conditions softened at the end of the Ice Age.

If you have the geological eye you will notice that there is something amiss in the lie of the land. The escarpment seems to take a step nearer to the river. A little tapping will disclose a knoll made of basalt, followed by open ground to the east, with another basalt knoll stepped south towards the river. You have crossed a line of fault, and this is how faults can often be traced on the surface. Of course, here we have basalt which is pretty tough; had the rocks been of a softer nature there might have been little change in the topography to provide a clue.

Further to the east there are some old limestone quarries where fossils can be found. It is perhaps easier to find them in the dry stone walls where weathering has brought them out. Over to the north there is a limestone pavement, poor compared with those of the Yorkshire Dales, but it is the only bit of grike country we have hereabouts. On the pavement there are some fine erratics of B.V.S.

N.B. The section here described is as it was some 25 years ago. Now it has become a very fine example of the work of erosion! The small falls have been washed away. Once the thin bands of calcite mudstone were gone there was little to resist the floods of recent years. The four feet of breccia that caused the fourth fall can now be seen spread out on the floor of the ghyll and the calcite mudstones, with their fossils, must be sought in the banks of the stream.

E.H.S., January, 1975.

11.   Ennerdale

ENNERDALE, like the Carrock Fell area, is rather remote and difficult of access. This is a pity. It is one of the loveliest of our dales and is geologically interesting too. I propose to approach it from the west, starting out from where the Cockermouth-Egremont road leaves Rowrah in the direction of Lamplugh (Grid Ref. 059187). After crossing the bridge over the disused railway a side road leaves the main road on the right and leads to Kirkland. Let us follow this road. At the crossroads by the little school you are in classic limestone country. The road to the right leads to the Salter Hall and Eskett quarries; the one on the left to Kelton Head, all in the Fourth limestone. Here the limestone beds are dipping away from the fells towards the sea so, as we approach Kirkland, we are crossing the outcrop of older and older limestones. The road straight ahead passes between limestone walls, the stones of which show to perfection "diagonally bedded sands", a strong current phase of the Seventh or oldest limestone. Across the fields, but hidden by a wood, is the disused series of quarries known as Stockhow Hall (Grid Ref. 067175) and here the Sixth and Fifth limestones can be seen. Following the road we come to another crossroads in Kirkland and here we go straight across and into the dip by the little church. The road rises now and at the corner where it turns sharp left you can look down towards Ennerdale Bridge. Just beneath you on your right, and parallel with the Kirkland-Ennerdale Bridge road, is a steep-sided, grass-grown gully.

To the observant eye this gully is somewhat incongruous for it contains no stream of sufficient size to have cut it—often it has no stream at all! How are we to account for it? To find an explanation we have to go back to the glacial period, and more particularly to the closing stages of that period. For a very long time our Lakeland had been sheathed in snow and ice, with great glaciers grinding down the valleys, and the coastal area invaded by masses of ice from the Irish Sea. The source of this ice sheet was the Scottish Highlands, and so we can often check its inland incursions by the erratics it has left on melting. Just as this northern ice sheet had acted as a barrier against our Lakeland ice, so now when the ice began to melt it acted as a barrier against the meltwaters, often damming them back to form sheets of impounded water and glacier lakes. We had one here in Ennerdale, and further north along the valley of the Marron there seems a good deal of evidence for further sheets.

As there was no easy escape to the west, many and often complicated courses were followed, with a general tendency to escape south across the fells towards Morecambe Bay. In the process the meltwaters cut a fine series of channels similar to the one you are looking at now and, while in the past these have always been described as "overflow channels", the inference being that they were cut AT THE SURFACE by the meltwaters, the tendency nowadays is to regard them as "sub-glacial channels" —that is channels cut BENEATH THE ICE. My own feeling is that in all probability there were channels of each kind and distinguishing one from the other will never be too easy! However, it is thought that at one time the Irish Sea ice stood so high across the mouth of Ennerdale that the meltwaters cut a notch on the southern watershed at around one thousand feet. But the Irish Sea ice was itself shrinking and as it did so it retreated up the coast of Cumberland so that open water came steadily northwards. This had two effects—the height of the ice barrier fell, and with it the level of the glacier lakes. As time went on the meltwater escaped across lower and lower watersheds to find its way into the sea further and further up the coast. On the fells opposite, between Ennerdale Bridge and Calder Bridge, there is a very fine series of channels which includes the Nanny-catch Gorge, Uldale and the Haile-Stocksbridge Gorge.

The channel we are considering here at Kirkland was cut at a late stage in the melting of the ice, a stage when the retreat up the coast had gone far enough to release the entrapped water in Ennerdale but not far enough to free some of the water to the north. Tongues of ice were still being pushed over the cols from the Buttermere valley and the meltwater from some of these would help too.

Walking along in the direction of Ennerdale it is not long before the lake comes into view below. The lake bed has been over-deepened by ice action and the waters dammed back by morainic material left as the ice melted. Conspicuous upon the further shore is Angler's Crag, backed by the steep Crag Fell. Examining this fell side carefully you will notice that it is cut across by several steps that run roughly parallel with the lake beneath. It would seem as if the whole fell side has slipped bodily forward towards the lake to leave these steps, the marked over-deepening of the lake having left an unstable fell side above.

Further along we come to some old mine tips on the left-hand side of the road. These are the spoil heaps of an old haematite mine, Kelton Head (Grid Ref. 083182), worked mainly during the First World War. If you desire a specimen of Cumberland haematite, a little seeking hereabouts should provide one. Should you have no luck here you might try the tips of the Knockmurton mines further over on the fell of that name, a new forestry road

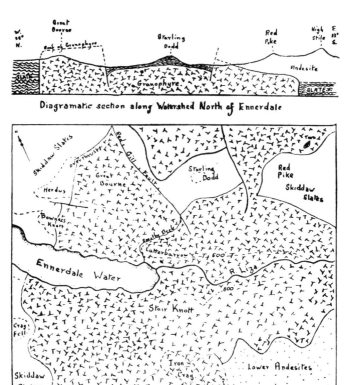

Diagramatic section along Watershed North of Ennerdale

Rough sketch map of Ennerdale and the Granophyre.
After the Geological Survey

giving easy access. Both these mines are of interest because the haematite occurs, not in limestone, as is usually the case both in West Cumberland and in Furness, but in veins in the Skiddaw Slates, some of which were twenty feet wide and went down for at least 500 feet.

The origin of our Cumberland haematites has always been a hotly debated subject with the generally held theory being that it has replaced limestone, carried to the place where it is now found by descending waters that had leached the mineral from the overlying red rocks of the Permo-Triassic. What then of veins like these in Skiddaw Slate that go down to such a depth? Or of similar veins on the other side of Ennerdale at the junction between the Slates and the Granophyre, or the old mines up at Boot in Eskdale where the ore was mined from the Eskdale

Granite? There are some very rich veins of haematite many feet wide in the B.V.S. between Esk Pike and Hanging Knotts in Ore Gap. It is an old climbing tale that the ore hereabouts deflects the compass, but I doubt it for rhaematite is non-magnetic.

As to the vexed question of the origin of the ore: I have known both the mines and the miners for many years now and I have never yet met a mine's man who agrees with this theory. He may not be able to put forward an alternative theory of his own but he often sums it up succinctly by saying, "You never find much ore far away from the fells". What he is saying, perhaps without realising it, is that you never find much ore far away from the great igneous masses. Generally speaking this has proved true, nor should it be forgotten that the same conditions (i.e. Permo-Triassic rocks overlying the Carboniferous limestone) can be found almost all round Lakeland, as well as in southern Scotland, with scarcely a trace of any ore! I wish I could say that the problem was easily settled but I fear this is not the case. Within the orebodies themselves there is such a wide variety of minerals indicating differing temperatures of deposition, while even the haematite occurs in at least two distinct temperature forms! I feel that our haematites offer a glorious opportunity for patient research both as to source and conditions of deposition . . . not to mention their true age.

Leaving the mines, press on towards the hamlet of Croasdale. As you descend the steep hill, with lovely views of the lake and the fells, look back towards the west and notice several flat topped mounds clinging to the fell side. These are described as "outwash deltas", places where streams from the melting ice swept glacial debris into the waters of Glacier Lake Ennerdale. They are mostly of sand and gravel, and it is from this kind of deposit that vast quantities of these materials are recovered for industry. Because the sand grains are unworn they are sharp and angular and thus give a better bond in making concrete structures.

To enter the little hamlet you have to cross the bridge over Croasdale Beck, and it is the upper reaches of this beck that provided the excellent photograph of "over-lapping spurs" in Arthur Holmes' famous book on physical geology. The lane leading from the hamlet towards the lake has undergone much improvement since this book was first written but even so it still demands care if you are going by car. Having safely negotiated the narrow twisting part of the road you will come out on a more open stretch with the crags of Bowness Knott straight in front of you. After the flat you cross a crude bridge over Rake Beck to come to a really atrocious piece of road. Narrow, and full of potholes, it certainly needs care but it will bring you across a cattle grid to a car park and picnic area, with Bowness Cottage across the fields.

Having parked the car, notice that the track from Bowness comes to the road, across which it continues into a quarry (Grid Ref. 110115) hidden by the wood. This is worth a little time; on entering through the trees you are faced by a rock wall at the foot of the screes with, on the left, some light coloured, almost white, boulders. These are as interesting as they are enigmatic for we do not know their exact source. The late Professor Hollingworth, who was responsible for this area when he worked on the Geological Survey, described them as boulders of pegmatite, "a coarse quartz albite rock with abundant crystals of apatite". He says he found crystals approaching one quarter of an inch in width and over an inch in length. Worth looking for, I think you will agree, but I must admit I have never found them so big, although smaller ones are common enough.

But what is pegmatite? Pegmatites are formed as a late phase in the cooling of acid igneous magmas and are usually injected in the form of veins, or dykes, into the surrounding rocks. Mostly composed, as here, of quartz and felspar, they are a common source of some of our more uncommon minerals, and although this rock is only known from these fallen blocks it is a fairly safe assumption to associate it with the nearby Buttermere and Ennerdale granophyre.

Now examine the back wall and the first thing to notice is that while the rock IS Skiddaw Slate, it is very tough and hard, and this is due to baking by the heat of the intrusion. If the wall is wet on the day of your visit you will see that it is penetrated by thin strings of pinkish material and this too has issued from the granophyre. If the wall is dry you will have to look very closely to spot these strings. Following the wall along, the rough track rises for about 25 paces, and in another 25 paces a dyke of dark coloured rock stands out from the wall. This too is probably an offshoot from the nearby igneous mass for the granophyre has, as we shall see later, a basic phase.

Leaving the quarry, cross the field and follow the rough track down by Bowness Cottage, to turn left right opposite where a gate gives access to the house (see map on page 90). Not far across the fell you will come to a rock wall above the gleaming lake beneath. If you examine this rock face you will see that it is composed of thinly bedded Skiddaw Slate, but so well baked as to make you hesitate. A climb of a few steps brings you to the foot of a wall of rock with a holly tree, and behind this there is a rounded and smoothed roche moutonnée. Keeping your eye open hereabouts you can hardly fail to spot bands of pinkish coloured rock crossing the path. These are felsite dykes intruded into the hardened slates. At this point the roche moutonnée is crossed by a depression, with direct progress blocked by a wall of rock, at the foot of which there is still another felsite dyke.

Climbing to the top you can see that the upstream end of the mound is rounded and smoothed while the downstream faces have been plucked by the ice. The ground to the east slopes down between the road and the lake and is composed of glacial drift which effectually hides the junction between the slates and the granophyre, but you can find exposures of this rock by the side of the road as you head towards the lake. Breaking a piece off you will find a rather fine grained pinkish coloured rock which shows but little structure; this is a marginal variety of the granophyre and it has cooled much too quickly for its true characteristic to develop. If we would see the normal granophyre we must go up the dale away from the junction and as the scenery is so very lovely a walk along the lake is well worth while.

As you walk along notice the fell on the other side of the lake. The rough Crag Fell is mostly baked Skiddaw Slate with the junction running down the eastern flank. From here along the skyline to the east notice the smooth outline, typical of most fells composed of our local granophyre. Of course the fell-top has been well glaciated but the character of the rock has much to do with it too. At the head of the lake you can see the same rounded fells but backed by the sharp crags of Pillar. This sudden change in the scenery we can equate with the geological structure for, while the rounded fells are granophyre, Pillar and its neighbours are composed of tough volcanic lavas, bits of which, transported by ice, now litter the roadside along the lake. Having passed the shallow embayment, surrounded almost by trees and with a picnic table kindly provided by the Forestry Commission, we come to a stream which goes beneath the road. This is Smithy Beck, and the name is indicative of something you may care to see, for if you go down the left bank of the stream and look carefully among the bracken you will find, half hidden by the turf, little mounds with many unusual looking stones. Dark brown in colour, they are noticeably heavy. They look as if at some time they have been molten, as indeed they have for this is "slag" and where you are standing is the site of an old "bloomery", a place where long ago man made his early efforts at extracting iron from its ore by smelting with charcoal.

Beyond Smithy Beck and the Forest Gate, the granophyre crops out by the roadside. It is a light pink in colour with bits of glassy quartz and splotches of a green mineral; this is chlorite, an altered mica. There may or may not be recognisable felspars as the rock is very variable and often you have to look to find a bit showing them. Some varieties are quite porphyritic with well developed felspar crystals, but these are highly complex, both plagioclase and orthoclase being present. Not only are the felspars, particularly the orthoclase, intergrown with the quartz as we discussed up at Carrock, but the felspars themselves intergrow to form what is known as "perthitic structure". Looking at the rock in the mass you can see that it is well jointed and this has aided the destructive force of ice plucking during glacial times. As a result, the Ennerdale granophyre is one of the commonest of our Lake District erratics, and pieces, even big boulders of it, are quite common in the drift as far south as the Midlands.

Like most of the large igneous masses of the Lake District its form and age have been much disputed. The older workers tended to regard it as a laccolith but when last examined by the Survey in the 1920s they concluded it was a stock, or batholith. This type of intrusion is steep-sided and does not conform to the bedding into which it has been emplaced. The map and section on page 84 we owe to the Survey and a little study will show that, by walking the ridge from east to west along the Buttermere side of the valley, one will pass from Borrowdales on High Stile to granophyre between that peak and Starling Dodd. The Dodd itself is Skiddaw Slate, much altered of course by heat of contact, but on the whole suggesting that like many of our Lakeland intrusions, advantage has been taken of the line of weakness at the contact between the Skiddaw Slates and the overlying Volcanics. Continuing along the ridge towards Great Borne one crosses a fault back on to granophyre, only to pass suddenly back on to Skiddaw Slates west of the summit as one crosses the junction. In places in making this traverse you will be walking over the original roof of the intrusion and, watching the rocks carefully, you may well find places where bits of the volcanics have been caught up in the granophyre to form "xenoliths", as they are called. The age of the intrusion is problematical and has been much argued about; Devonian seems to find most favour and while a piece of granophyre has recently been found in the Brockram it is only one pointer (radio-metric dating is in progress.)   This ridge walk is very well worth doing but I think we had better leave it for another day and take time over it!

Go back now down the lake, pick up the car, carefully negotiate the bad bit of road and, having crossed Rake Beck, park nearby on the flat. It is Rake Beck that we wish to follow up so make your way to the streamside; here you can either follow the streamcourse or the much easier path up the hillside by the tree on the left bank. If you follow the stream you will see many exposures in the bed, all of which are Skiddaw Slate, but for the most part showing signs of alteration by heat. A minor streamcourse comes down from between Bowness Knott and Brown Howe to join the Rake Beck itself. I say "a streamcourse" because in dry weather this stream is often non-existent, but follow this tributary up from the junction keeping your eye on the left bank. The first exposure is much like the ones downstream, Skiddaw Slate, except that it is not only well baked but tends to have a slightly pinkish look. The next exposure, however, shows a completely different rock—a strong dyke of pink felsite with a clearly developed "spherulitic" structure. If you examine the exposure carefully, particularly near the upstream edge, you will find what look like little clusters of peas—these are the "spherules". On the whole the edges of these dykes seem to show the structure better than the middle, and this seems to be generally true of the many similar dykes that are associated with our intrusions in our western dales.

As to how these spherules are formed there seems little information available. Text books describe the structure minutely but have little to say as to what causes the phenomenon. Myself I wonder if an analogy from water engineering might not have some relevance. When water flows through a pipe, or conduit, the body of moving liquid towards the centre tends to flow in straight parallel lines. It has a "streamlike flow", but along the edges of the pipe or conduit, and the rougher the internal surface the more pronounced this is, the flow is described as "turbulent" —it moves along in little eddies. Remembering that the felsitic material of the dyke was injected in a liquid state, might not a similar explanation hold?

All the way up to the col the path runs between the stream-course and the forest fence and there are many rock exposures, mostly Skiddaw Slate, but often so well baked and shot through with faint strings of felsite that one hesitates at times. On the col itself there are good exposures on the Brown Howe side and stringers of white quartz are much in evidence. Over the fence among the trees there is a marked depression, followed by the stream (if there is one!), for this is a line of weakness caused by a fault which displaces the junction between the slates and the granophyre to the east, but the evidence for this is now hidden by the trees of the forest.

A forest ride runs across this depression in the direction of the lake and this leads to the area we wish to explore. The stile here we owe to the kindness of the Forestry Commission and in accepting their hospitality please, please do remember that we owe them our care and consideration. The floor of the ride is clothed with heather and in dry weather will get like tinder, so put out your cigarettes and guard against the greatest danger, and the forester's biggest worry—fire.

Having crossed the dip to where the land begins to rise keep a sharp look out for a small exposure which crosses the ride. A piece broken off here shows a very lovely rock, pink in colour but shot through with dark green to almost black crystals. This is the "needle rock", as described by Rastall in his paper on the granophyre. The long needle-like crystals are augites, and he

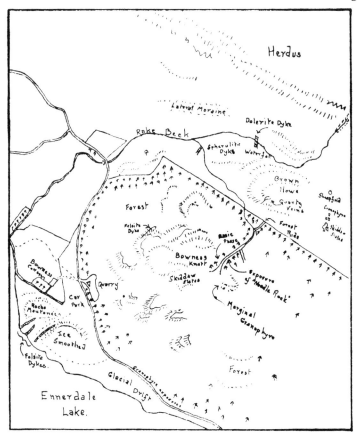

Rough Sketch Map of Bowness Knott area.
E. H. Shackleton. F.G.S.

ascribes the rock to an interaction between the granophyre proper and a basic phase of the intrusion. An old wall, or at least its remains, crosses the ride and not far beyond on the right, but screened by the trees to some extent, there is a good exposure which shows the basic phase very well. Dark grey in colour and of a fine grain, notice that fingers of more light coloured granophyric materials are intruded into it. This suggests that the basic phase was the first to be intruded, closely followed by the granophyre itself. This seems to be the usual order of intrusion and many of our granitic rocks in and around Lakeland show it. A little beyond this exposure the trees end and here the Skiddaw Slates of the Knott are well exposed, while towards the lake but lower down the fell on the eastern side, granophyre can be seen.

Return now to the fence and make your way towards the old sheepfold, noticing that there is a grassy patch surrounded by bracken with rock exposures upon it. The nearest outcrop, however altered, is Skiddaw Slate, but only a few feet away there are typically blocky exposures of the granophyre. The actual junction between the two rocks has been mapped as running up the fell side to the west of the sheepfold but the scree cover makes it difficult if not impossible to trace. The best place to look would be well up the fell side in the vicinity of the gully which is the source of Rake Beck, for here the rocks are better exposed. On the other hand even the officers of the Survey found it next to impossible to lay down a certain line of junction, so inextricably mixed up are the rocks!

In making your way back there is one other exposure which is worth seeing. Following the beck (with care for the ground is rough) you will pass between walls of altered Skiddaw Slate while the stream plunges over one fall after another. The biggest fall is caused by a well developed dyke but this time of a doleritic character. If there is not too much water you can get a sample at the fall.

Now this is not by any means an exhaustive exposition of the geology of Ennerdale, for even here in the vicinity of Rake Beck, I have only indicated the most easily found exposures. The dykes mentioned have extensions you may care to seek out, if you have the time. Perhaps you have noted the long mound which runs along the foot of the screes of Herdus. This has been alternatively described as a lateral moraine or as snow slumped scree. If you were to examine it with care perhaps you could decide which is the more likely?

13.   Fossils and Fossil Localities

IN the previous pages mention has been made on many occasions of fossils to be found in the rocks of Lakeland. For the most part these have been in reference to the Skiddaw Slates where, because of the age of these rocks and the rough treatment they have had in the intervening ages, the finding of fossils is not an easy matter. Besides the Skiddaw Slates there are later rocks in which the chance of finding well preserved fossils is somewhat better, but before directing your footsteps to these localities I think I might give a little time to the subject of fossils, besides telling you of such localities in the Skiddaw Slates where you might look for them.

This subject is a big one; it comprises a science in itself, the science of Palaeontology. Obviously I can do no more than attempt to make some sense of the subject. Even if long ago the weirdest notions were entertained as to the origin of fossils, we now recognise them as the remains of once-living things which have been entombed in accumulating sediments, and thus preserved. It is from these remains that we have been able to piece together the story of evolving life over the ages. Generally speaking this story is one of increasing complexity; as a result the older the rocks we have to deal with, the simpler are the forms of life preserved in them as fossils.

We have seen that the Skiddaw Slates are very, very old, and the questions which arise are: what kind of life flourished all those hundreds of millions of years ago, and what kind of record has been left upon the rocks? Going back in geological time beyond our oldest Lakeland rocks, we find the Pre-Cambrian rocks referred to as "Azoic", meaning "without life". However, in recent years undoubted fossils have been found even in these rocks. While these finds are mostly algal, rather lowly plant remains, they are undoubted fossils and some of them discovered in Canada take us back little short of two thousand million years! The importance of this will appear in the sequel.

The first easily-recognisable fossils are to be found in the Cambrian rocks, and these show such a comparatively high state of development that they must have had a long, long line of more simple predecessors. First steps are slow and halting and it comes as no surprise to find that the developmental stage reached by life in Cambrian times had a pre-history several times longer than all the myriad developments since. That most of these early life forms have left scant trace is certain, if disappointing, and seems largely due to the fact that for long these lowly creatures either had no need for hard parts, or had not as yet learned the trick of secreting them.

It was with the Cambrian that a marked change took place, for it is in these rocks that we first find living things that do develop hard parts and so become capable of ready fossilization. What is interesting about these early remains is the high standard of development that is implied. The realization of this came only slowly; in fact, it was not until the 1920s when, in some Cambrian shales in the Burgess Pass of British Columbia, fossils were found in such a high state of preservation that it was possible to work out in detail their complete anatomy. When this had been done it was a shock to find that these hitherto considered "lowly creatures" could match, part for part, the anatomy of the most highly developed creatures of their kind today.

Several types of animal left remains in these early Cambrian times. The most important were the trilobites (see page 72) and they have been so called because their bodies were characterised by three well marked lobes. They had learned the trick of covering their soft parts with a segmented carapace which, like many creatures of today, they shed from time to time. It is this discarded carapace which is most often found, the complete organism being far more rare. It tended to mislead early workers as to the true complexity of the trilobite.

This armoured cover which we now find fossilized was composed of a substance called chitin, a horny substance, somewhat similar to our fingernails, and it is interesting to note that Cambrian creatures, be they trilobites, graptolites or shellfish, all used it. Later sea creatures used calcium carbonate. Why? Were the early seas deficient in calcium? Or was it that early living things never learned the trick of extracting and utilizing it? Besides the delicately toughened parts of the trilobite's exterior, it had internal organs of great refinement, with gills, renal organs, digestive tract and blood circulation. For seeing, many of them had comparatively large eyes, often with compound lenses, similar to those of a fly.

The remains of these creatures are first found in Cambrian Rocks, but they continued to evolve to reach their acme late in Ordovician times, after which they began to dwindle in size and in numbers, and died out almost completely by Carboniferous times. Fossil trilobites have been found in the Skiddaw Slates but by no means so frequently as we should like.

Along with the trilobites, though perhaps a little later, another group came into prominence, the graptolites. Originally the word was "grapholite", for very often their remains look like delicately

GRAPTOLITES FROM THE SKIDDAW SLATES.

Didymograptus nitidus (Hall)
Forestry roads. Skiddaw Dodd.

Didymograptus fractus (Salter)
(Extensiform type)
Screes of White Horse.

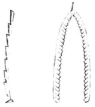

Atygograptus lapworthi.
Hodason Howe Quarry.
Knott Head Whinlatter.

Didymograptus bifidus.(Hall)
(Tuning fork type)
Screes of White Horse.

Didymograptus gibberulus (Nicholson)
(Recurved type)
Screes of Great Knott.

Tetragraptus quadribrachiatus. (Hall)
Knott Head Whinlatter. Screes of
White Horse. Barf Thornthwaite.

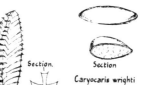

Dichograptus octobrachiatus (Hall)
Forestry roads Skiddaw Dodd.

Glossograptus.
Forestry roads.
Skiddaw Dodd.

Section.

Section

Caryocaris wrighti
A phyllopod.
Screes of White Horse.

Diplograptus pristiniformis (Hall)
Whinlatter Pass.
Barf Thornthwaite.
Forestry roads Skiddaw Dodd.

Phyllograptus typus.(Hall)
Whinlatter Pass and Barf.

Drawings by H. Shackleton

done drawings in pencil upon the rocks. This group has always been somewhat puzzling, but it has also been very useful for, after a slow start, it went through fairly rapid evolutionary changes. Free floating as they were, each new type was rapidly dispersed about the seas of their times and their remains, sinking to the bottom, became entombed in the successive layers of sediment to provide a very efficient index to the rocks of late Cambrian, Ordovician and Silurian age.

What were the graptolites? What were they like? The second question is far easier to answer than the first. Often they look like compound leaves of grass, united at one end and with each leaf, or stipe, as it is called, having a markedly serrated edge. Each tooth provided a receptacle in which lived a polyp with delicate waving tentacles that caught minute unicellular organisms as they floated by. Through each stipe ran a connecting canal, apparently giving intercommunication from polyp to polyp. It is thought that the graptolite hung down in the water from some kind of float, but this I have never seen. Probably it was too delicate for ready preservation.

The graptolites started off as compound creatures with up to as many as 32 stipes, and development followed the line of a progressive reduction of this number from 32 to 16, 16 to eight, eight to four, four to two and finally, in Silurian times, to one. On the face of it this seems like a contradiction of the general evolutionary rule of increasing complexity, but this is probably misleading. It simply means that we do not as yet know enough about the life and development of graptolites.

The above description, along with the many drawings, should give some idea what the graptolites were like. Their great use, as has been mentioned, is the indication they give of the relative age of the rocks in which they are found. To ascertain this you need not be an expert palaeontologist. All that is necessary is to find the fossils, carefully note the most prevalent form and its number of stipes. Generally speaking, the greater the number of stipes, the older are the rocks. Silurian graptolites have only one stipe, upper Silurian ones are mostly straight or slightly curved, middle Silurian graptolites are mixed, some straight, some curved, while in the lower Silurian the curved forms predominate. In the upper Ordovician many types have two stipes and these are bent backwards away from each other. In the middle Ordovician there are many two-branched graptolites also, but the stipes for the most part face each other, or are bent back horizontally.

The lower Ordovician is marked by many stiped forms, mostly fours and eights. Cambrian graptolites are not so common but when found are multiple stiped, so without a textbook and without even knowing their names you have at least a rough guide to a large slice of earth history. Be warned that you cannot make determinations on one solitary fossil; it is the prevalent type you need. If all you have is one lone fossil anything might have happened to it. It may look straight when in fact it is a broken piece of what was once a long curved form.

What were these interesting creatures? This is not an easy question to answer. For a long time they were regarded as hydramedusae, popularly known as "sea mosses". By some experts they were looked upon as the forerunners of the corals, but recent investigations tend to place them with the proto-chordates, the far-off predecessors of the vertebrates, to which class we ourselves belong. However this may be, after a long and successful run they, like the trilobites, ceased to be. Possibly they both went down before the eurypterids and the cephalopods. The former were lobster-like creatures which reached the remarkable size of eight feet. The latter were octopus-like creatures. The remains of both have been found in the Skiddaw Slates.

Living in these early seas was a small shellfish, the lingula. Rather like a small mussel in appearance, it lived buried in the mud and its shell was also chitinous. The little lingula extends a challenge for, starting its career almost six hundred million years ago, it has successfully outlived its competitors to the present day. Through all the great changes of land and sea, living alongside a long succession of more and more highly specialised creatures, it has quietly persisted in its secluded life, unchanged for hundreds of millions of years. Its organisation is simple. It may have found no need to change in a changing world. Other creatures living in the same environment have come and gone to leave no living representatives. Why has lingula survived? It looks as if, 100 years after Darwin, there is still a great deal we do not know about evolution!

So much for the life of the times. How, and where should we look for the evidence? The many sketches may help, but I strongly advise a visit to the Keswick Museum where the curator will show you specimens gathered from the local rocks. To search for anything, no matter what, having only the haziest notion of what it looks like, is not conducive to success. Having familiarized yourself with the appearance of trilobites and graptolites, where should you search?

For the Upper Ordovician and the Lower Silurian I can indicate suitable places to look, and be reasonably specific. For the Skiddaw Slates it is not so easy. All I can do is to give some guidance and mention some localities where I have myself found specimens. Remembering that the Slates have suffered much from crushing, it is best to avoid highly contorted and cleaved beds. Fossils, if present, are usually spoilt and indeterminate. Generally speaking the darker shales are more productive than the lighter coloured ones, and while fossils do occur in the sandy beds they are rarely well preserved.

Near Keswick there are a few localities of interest. At Hodgson How Quarry, just beyond Portinscale, graptolites have been found. This is the "type locality" for Azygograptus; in other words, where it was first found. It is rather a delicate graptolite, it needs looking for, and is perhaps best seen when the rocks are wet.

Along the line of the Whinlatter Pass there are numerous exposures, and while cleavage is a bit troublesome several kinds of graptolite can be found. Near the top of the rise, going up from Braithwaite, just before taking the bend at the top of Knott Head, there is a small quarry on the left-hand side of the road. Here I have found Azygograptus and Tetragraptus in a fair state of preservation. In the bank just above the quarry I have got reasonably good Didymograptus of the extensiform type. Round the bend, where cars often stop for the view down on to Bassenthwaite, Phyllograptus occurs rather sparingly, but can be found in greater numbers above Coomb Bridge. At the other end of the pass, at the bottom of the steep descent, there is a large quarry in the Skiddaw Slates. Here, high up, one bedding plane literally swarms with graptolites, but elsewhere in the quarry they are sparse.

At Thornthwaite, on the slopes of Barf, graptolites can be found in the scree material. They are affected to some extent by cleavage but Phyllograptus, Bryograptus, Tetragraptus and Clonograptus are reported from here.

Some of the best localities are on the slopes of Skiddaw itself, particularly above Bassenthwaite village. One mile S.E. of Bassenthwaite Halls, in the screes of White Horse, you may look for "tuning fork" graptolites in blue black shales with little cleavage. Tetragraptus occurs here also along with the crustacean Caryocaris. The screes of Great Knott, a little further over, yield similar fossils and many worm tracks, but perhaps one of the locations of easiest access is on Skiddaw Sand Beds. This location is on Skiddaw Dodd and the forestry people have cut access roads all along the steep hillside. In doing so they have laid open numerous exposures of Slate and many yield graptolites. At one place or another here I have found Didymograptus, Dichograptus, Tetragraptus and Diplograptus. If you are not too lucky with the fossils you will be rewarded with some magnificent views, but please remember the danger of fire. It is a constant worry to the foresters in dry weather.*

I have found that the most profitable method of collecting fossils is to carefully examine the material lying about at any exposure, for then the fossils have had time to weather out. Failing this you will need a hammer; not too heavy, with a square head at one side and a chisel edge at the other (preferably with the edge at right angles to the shaft); a lens with which to examine the finds; a bag of some sort in which to carry them; and plenty of good newsprint in which to wrap them. Many a good fossil has been destroyed by rubbing against another. On the paper in which you wrap the specimen, write clearly the location at which you found it. It is of little use trying at the end of a long and tiring day to remember just where you found a certain specimen. You rarely can with any certainty and fossils (however good they may be) lose much of their value if you cannot pin-point where they came from.

As regards the Skiddaw Slates, fossils do take looking for. These rocks are very, very old and fossil remains are nowhere prolific. On the other hand, it is often the veriest amateur who has the luck. My wife usually beats me when it comes to finding graptolites and trilobites!

* It has been pointed out to me by the Forestry Commission that whilst there is no right of way on to Skiddaw Dodd, permission can be obtained on application to:- The Head Forester, Piel Wyke, Bassenthwaite. Tel. Bass. Lake 272.

14.   Ambleside and Skelgill

A GLANCE with a discerning eye at the scenery around the head of Windermere is enough to lead one to expect a different geological formation. At the head of the lake stands the rough upstanding Loughrigg Fell. South of this the scenery changes abruptly, becoming well wooded and more pastoral. Loughrigg is composed of Borrowdale Volcanics, hard tough rocks that are slow to break down and produce only a thin layer of soil at best. The country to the south is on rocks of Silurian age. These rocks are considerably softer; they weather more quickly, and produce a much more useful soil covering. As a result contours are softer, vegetation is more lush and, in the woodlands, hardwoods tend to replace conifers.

Travel south from Waterhead to a little beyond the *Low Wood Hotel* on the lake side. Here a by-road on the left leaves the main road and climbs steeply. It leads through Troutbeck in Westmorland to the Kirkstone Pass, but before reaching the village turn off on the road marked on the map as The Old Hundreds (Grid Ref. 400022). Unless you want to get in a mess, make this part of the journey on foot, for I doubt if The Old Hundreds has had much attention since the days when it got its name! Follow the road as it climbs and winds between stone walls across the fell side. About one mile from the start there is a stile on the left (Grid Ref. 397024) giving access to a path that leads, by Skelgill, to Jenkins Crag. Follow this path across the fields in the direction of the wooded ravine.

From this footpath you have fine views of Windermere, backed by the Coniston Old Man, Wetherlam, and the rocky peaks of the Scafell range. To the right are the well known Langdales. All these greater heights are, of course, B.V.S., but it is the softer rolling country beneath that is our immediate interest. Notice on the western shore of Windermere the deep embrasure of Pull Wyke. This little bay has been cut from the comparatively soft shales of the Skelgill Beds that we are going to see, the lowest beds of the Silurian System.

After crossing the fields the path drops steeply down into the wood to an old stone bridge. Here you can dump your haversack and get out your hammer. Above the bridge, on the left bank, is a steep cliff about sixty feet in height. Below the bridge there is a waterfall and, on the same bank of the stream, a ten foot cliff. We will start with the lower exposure.

One can, with a little care, get down to the water level on the right bank and here the water glides over a tough grey rock. If you can break it with your hammer you will find a rubbly argillaceous limestone—the Flexuosa Limestone. It is so called after a fossil shell, Atrypa Flexuosa, but specimens are extremely difficult to find here. Now look carefully at the bank of dark shales above the stream. About one foot from the base there is a slip plane. Roughly one foot above this lies another, with fault breccia at the northern end. The slip planes are almost horizontal faults, places where the beds have slipped over one another. In a small way they are thrust planes and can be seen on close inspection as dark marks running across the exposure. These are only minor slips but they are complementary to a much larger one between the Flexuosa Limestone and the underlying Ashgillian rocks. This larger fault is always present at this horizon wherever these beds are exposed and it is this line of weakness in the rocks that the stream has found and followed.

Look carefully about fifteen inches above the second slip plane and you will find a pale green band. It is only a fraction of an inch thick, but is of great interest. When examined petrologically this "green streak", as it has been called, turns out to be composed of very fine volcanic detritus. It will be remembered that a good deal of Ordovician time was given up to great volcanic activity in many parts of Britain; this was followed by quieter times when vulcanicity died away and more normal deposits were accumulated. That activity was not entirely ended is suggested by this "green streak", which is found over a very wide area. It probably denotes an outburst of Krakatoan type, a great volcanic explosion that scattered dust far and wide. The interesting thing about the streak is that it is always found at this particular horizon.

In saying that this green streak is widespread at this horizon, what exactly are we implying? That we always find a green streak in beds that look like these over a wide area does not prove in itself that these streaks were deposited in the same interval of time. What we are relying on here is fossil evidence. This bed of dark shale which we are considering took a very long time to accumulate and during that time one kind of living thing, the graptolite, was undergoing rapid evolutionary change; as a result different beds contain markedly different kinds of graptolite. The beds before us contain a graptolite to which the name Dimorphograptus confertus has been given, and for short the beds are spoken of as the confertus beds. As this fossil has been found at many different and widespread localities, along with the green streak, we feel pretty confident in stating that the same eruption caused the streak in each case for in these beds, and in these beds only, is Dimorphograptus confertus commonly found.

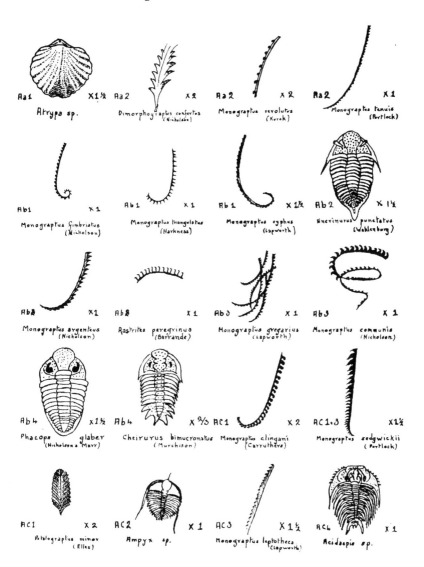

Some Fossils from the Skelgill Beds

Finding the type fossil at this particular place is very difficult, but we have it on no less authority than that of Marr and Nicholson that the type fossil has been found here, and at other localities close by. The same shales crop up in the opposite bank; they are easier to get at, and graptolites are common, but I have always found D. confertus elusive.

Above the confertus beds there is a belt of fault breccia (seen as an almost black patch in the bank a little further downstream). This is another line of shear where the beds have slipped over one another under the pressure of earth movements long after consolidation. Above this breccia there is a band of dark shales about six feet thick, the type fossil of which is Monograptus fimbriatus, and this you should look for using the sketch of the fossil as a guide. If I have never had much luck with D. confertus, I have often found good specimens of M. fimbriatus, and it should be remembered that at any location showing exposures of these beds the two type fossils occur in the same relative positions.

Moving now above the bridge (the "lower" bridge, Marr calls it, for there is another one upstream which carried The Old Hundreds) we find an almost vertical cliff on the left bank, while on the right the stream comes round a bend and slides over the bedding planes. At this point the stream is gliding over the Ashgill Beds and fossil shells are not difficult to find. Conspicuous among them is Harknessella (Orthis) vespertillio, a fossil one usually finds in the Ashgill Beds. If you do not have much luck here, and do not wish to go to Ashgill you might try the upper part of Skelgill below the upper bridge.

Looking at the cliff on the left bank you will notice a deep-cut cleft at the upstream end. This is a fault, but a different kind of fault from the one associated with the confertus beds. Here it is not that the beds have slipped one over the other. The beds have actually been broken. There is a second cleft, though not so conspicuous, on the downstream side, and between these two "dip" faults, as they are called, the whole block has been dropped bodily down. As a result some of the lower beds are buried beneath the level of the stream.

About three feet six inches above the stream level there is a band of shale about eight inches thick. Grey in colour at the bottom, it becomes black and very hard at the top, and about three inches below the top is another green streak. This is the Monograptus argenteus band, and while characterised by this graptolite it contains many others, all in a high state of preservation. The difficulty is to get any of the rock out of the cliff for examination. Seventy years ago Professor Marr was complaining about this. I can only agree, while at the same time pointing out that with the requisite equipment, i.e. heavy hammers and chisels, it can be done.

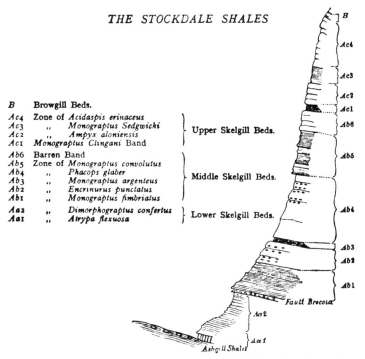

THE STOCKDALE SHALES

B	**Browgill Beds.**	
Ac4	Zone of *Acidaspis erinaceus*	
Ac3	,, *Monograptus Sedgwicki*	Upper Skelgill Beds.
Ac2	,, *Ampyx aloniensis*	
Ac1	*Monograptus Clingani* Band	
Ab6	Barren Band	
Ab5	Zone of *Monograptus convolutus*	
Ab4	,, *Phacops glaber*	
Ab3	,, *Monograptus argenteus*	Middle Skelgill Beds.
Ab2	,, *Encrinurus punctatus*	
Ab1	,, *Monograptus fimbriatus*	
Aa2	,, *Dimorphograptus confertus*	Lower Skelgill Beds.
Aa1	,, *Atrypa flexuosa*	

Fig. 9. Section across Skelgill (scale 15 ft to 1 in.).

For those who might wish to delve into the literature, I should explain that the expert would hardly refer to these as beds, i.e. confertus beds, etc. He would use the word zone. Thus, whilst we might refer to the M. argenteus band, it is as well to know that it is also the argenteus zone. Zonal fossils, to be of any use for this purpose, have to have a short range in geological time and they must, during that comparatively short time, become widespread in their occurrence. When I say that in addition to these characteristics such fossils also need to have some readily recognisable feature, it becomes obvious that not just any fossil can be used for the purpose of zoning. Here at Skelgill we are on a piece of classic ground, where the zones were worked out long ago by professional geologists, but it is often the gifted amateur who makes a great contribution to such work. Often he lives near the beds he is working on and does not mind how much time he devotes to them; there is, and always will be, room in our science for such people.

To get back to our area. Where the path slopes down to the bridge the M. convolutus and the M. sedgewicki zones are exposed, but again it takes patience to get the fossils and while I give Professor Marr's section on the previous page, I cannot claim to have traced all the zones. This is particularly the case with the trilobites, with which I have never had much luck. At one time or another I have done fairly well with the graptolites.

You could scarcely have a more delightful place than this in which to hunt. There are many exposures, both above and below the lower bridge, along the line of the ghyll, and also in some of the tributaries. Do not leave a mess behind you. It takes only a few minutes to clean up when you have got your fossils, but it is a job that should not be left to others.

If you go back by the way you have come, the many little quarries in the fields are in the Brathay Flags, the next higher division in the Silurian overlying the Stockdale Shales. The succession here runs: Ashgill Shales (highest member of the Ordovician), Skelgill Beds, Browgill Beds (which together form the Stockdale Shales) and then the Brathay Beds, all of which are Silurian. The Browgill Beds here are poorly represented at the top of the slope up from the bridge, while the Brathay Beds in the fields yield fossils only on one or two bedding planes. Where they occur they are numerous. The exact horizons are difficult to find.

N.B.: During the summer of 1974 the Cumberland Geological Society visited Skelgill and a splendid trilobite was found. We also examined the exposures of Coniston limestone by the path to the north.

15.   Ashgill, near Coniston

ASHGILL, the type locality of the Ashgillian, lies on the rough uplands above Torver, S.W. of Coniston. Leaving the main Coniston - Broughton-in-Furness road at Torver,* follow the lane up the hill and take the first turning left. This will bring you to what is half road, half watercourse, and to a tumble-down gate. Follow this road noticing the upturned edges of the Silurian rocks as you go. It is much easier to leave this old road by the little wood and follow the footpath. This will bring you out on to what is usually a wet, soggy moorland, with a marked depression running roughly north and south. This depression is caused by the outcrop, hidden beneath the peat, of the softer Skelgill and Browgill Beds. Higher up, on the horizon, there are some quarry tips. The tips mark the site of the old Ashgill Quarry (Grid Ref. 269954), long since abandoned. Before you reach the quarry you will come to the remains of a bridge across the beck and in the bank you will see some greenish shales. These are Browgill Beds and while they have some fossiliferous bands, they are not easy to find.

The most notable feature at Ashgill Quarry is a waterfall and the section you have come to see starts above this fall. Having surmounted the fall, follow the stream to where it makes a pronounced bend. Above this bend the stream shows shales in its banks for a little way before they become buried by drift. These are the Calymene Shales, the upper part of the so-called Coniston Limestone Series. I say so-called because, while there are limestone bands in the series, at most places Coniston Limestone consists of calcareous shale. The Coniston Limestone succeeds the Borrowdale Volcanics for the most part unconformably. This unconformity is nowhere easy to demonstrate and was in fact for long disputed, but if the dip of the beds of the two series is carefully observed they do not coincide—as the geologist would say—the strikes of the two series are incongruent. This implies that there was an interval of time, some earth movement and erosion between the deposition of the two—how long a time, it is difficult to say. (See "Geological Excursions in Lakeland".)

Search in the shales exposed above the bend should disclose

* Grid Ref. 284941

some fossils. Fossil shells, Orthis, Strophomena, Leptaena and Plectambonites have all been recorded and a specimen of one or more should not be too difficult to find. But the type fossil, Calymene planimarginata (a trilobite) is another matter. Unlike some trilobites this particular one is a fair size and there should be no difficulty in seeing it, but so far I have not been lucky here up on Ashgill. This, along with Phacops (Chasmops) marri, is said to be common, but like most of the trilobites hereabouts they are confined to nodules in the shales and I have never found these very plentiful. The trouble is that until the weather gets at the shales the nodules do not show, and when the weather has done its work more often than not what is left is a series of holes where the nodules have been! This is not very helpful, I agree, but on the upland there are many exposures showing this state of affairs. I suggest that these exposures may be more rewarding. Remember, specimens of these trilobites have been found here!

Going downstream, the Calymene Shales are succeeded by about seven feet of different rocks—the Phillipsinella Beds. In contrast to the Calymene Shales, when unweathered, the Phillipsinella Shales are a deep blue in colour. The former are more of a grey-blue. Another point is that these rocks are very close jointed and tend to break into small pieces, which does not make fossil hunting any easier. Small brachiopods seem to be present to the exclusion of the larger ones, with Dalnamella the most common. Phillipsinella is a trilobite but being very small it is not easy to find. Both it and Staurocephalus are said by Professor Marr to be common. Acidaspis, Trinucleus, and Cheirurus have all been recorded but are admitted to be rare.

On the right bank of the stream, below the bend, a rocky eminence is formed by the so-called White Limestone. It is here about twelve feet in thickness and while its appearance belies its name there are other locations where it comes nearer to the description. It is said to be almost unfossiliferous but last time I visited Ashgill a number of specimens were found, mostly brachiopods and bryozoa.

Between the White Limestone and the top of the waterfall the banks of the stream are low and all the exposures are at or below the water level. Some sixteen feet of rocks have been measured and close examination has shown that they are bedded volcanic ash, demonstrating that Ordovician vulcanicity did not die out all at once.

At the fall, about six feet of greenish grey calcareous shale is exposed, and this is the upper part of the Mucronatus Beds. Ten feet of the same strata follow to form the middle part of the fall, and while the first six feet is only sparingly fossiliferous the middle part of the fall was described by Marr as "swarming with fossils". This statement is true, but needs qualification, for a

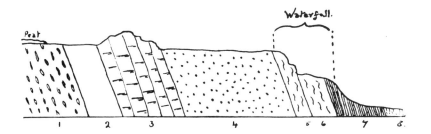

1. Calymene Beds.   2 Phillipsinella Beds.   3 White limestone.

4 Volcanic Ash.   5·6 Mucronatus Beds.   7 Ashgill Shales.
8. Skelgill Beds.

Section. Ashgill Beck.

Orthis (Harknessella) vespertillio J. de C. Sow.

Dalmanella elegantula. Dalman.

Orthis calligramma. Dalman.

Orthis lunata. J. de. C. Sowerby.

Plectambonites transversalis. Dalman.

Leptaena rhomboidalis Wilkins.

Calymene planimarginata. Reed.

Phillipsinella parabola. Barrande.

Staurocephalus globiceps. Portlock.

Trinucleus seticornis Hisinger. (Much enlarged)

Some Ashgillian Fossils.

strange thing happens here. While the rock is fresh and unweathered, fossils are almost indiscernible; when weathered, the rock breaks down to a comparatively soft "gingerbread" rock, and in this state the fossils are easy enough to see. The curious part about this phenomenon is that it is not confined to Ashgill; the same beds, even at far-away localities, display the same feature. There is also another qualification. Phacops (Dalmanites) mucronatus is only a small trilobite. Fragments are very common, but I have yet to find a complete one. There may be a head here, and a tail there, an eye perhaps, and broken plurae, but not complete trilobites. I make mention of this because what one finds depends a great deal on what one expects to find. A false picture in the mind's eye can be a pretty effective barrier to success.

The Mucronatus Beds are followed by the Ashgill Shales and these can best be explored in the big quarry. Fossils, mostly brachiopods with occasional bits of trilobites, are not uncommon if you are prepared to break up a bit of rock. As you enter the quarry from the waterfall you will notice a stream leaving it to join Ashgill; in a steep bank on the stream's right, darker shales are seen. These are the confertus beds of the overlying Skelgills, but again D. confertus seems hard to find.

Ashgill is a very exposed place, and my advice is to pick a reasonably warm day to make this trip. A shivering geologist, however enthusiastic he may be, can hardly be expected to have the patience to follow this sequence and to look for fossils. To do this with success will need both patience—and time. When you have had your fill of Ashgill itself, it is not far across the moor to Torver Beck. The upper part is a deep cut gully in the B.V.S. but lower down, where the ground begins to flatten out a little, there is a stone wall crossing the line of the beck. A few yards above this, on the right bank at stream level, you will find some dark shales. These are part of the M. Sedgewicki zone of the Skelgill Beds while just above the wall a nodular band containing Acidaspis crosses the beck but is not easy to find. This is the lowest bed of the Browgill Shales, and although some faulting interferes with the succession, the light-coloured beds that follow downstream are Browgills and you can see them cropping out for some way as you follow the stream back to Torver.

In these two excursions we have seen something of:

> The Lower Silurian
> The Upper Ordovician

somewhere about 150 feet of strata only. Much of it must have accumulated very slowly to give the rapid succession of graptolitic types. We have seen, but not examined, the Browgill Beds and the Brathay Flags. The deposits are about 1,200 feet thick, but overlying them we have the Upper Coniston Flags or Cold-well Beds (1,500 feet), the Coniston Grits (4,000 feet), the Bannisdale Slates (5,000 feet approximately), and the Kirkby Moor Flags (1,500 feet), all of which are Silurian. It is to the character of this vast series of deposits that we owe the gentle scenery of this part of Lakeland, and they represent the southern limb of a great anticline, the northern limb of which is for the most part lost.

Although the strata above the Browgill Beds have never had the detailed attention that they merit, the general faunal succession is known and merely stresses a geological mystery. Careful comparison of our graptolite fauna with the graptolites of other areas seems to indicate a far greater affinity with the fauna of North American palaeozoic rocks than with the graptolites of Wales. Why this should be so is not easy of explanation. There are, of course, many intriguing theories but we had better not start to elaborate them! Do we know enough about the real geography of those times, or about the habits of graptolites, particularly about the way in which they propagated themselves? It is just one illustration of the many fascinating problems that geology presents to the questing mind.

16. Identification of Rocks

GEOLOGY, like cricket, is best played in the field. No amount of reading will ever make you into a geologist. The only real road to expertness in the subject is to handle rocks, fossils and minerals, find specimens for yourself and have a try at identifying them. The difficulty of identifying what one finds can put off many people who would otherwise take an interest in the subject. In America, where the educational value of the science has found greater recognition than it has so far done in this country, many simplified schemes are in use for the identification of specimens. The only attempt I have seen here is in an admirable book on Field Geology by Himus and Sweeting, and this I can thoroughly recommend.

What help can be given towards the recognition of some of the specimens which may be found on these excursions? We will assume a rock specimen has been found and you desire to classify it. The obvious thing to do, so it would seem, is to take a good look at it and see if you can recognise some feature which will enable you to identify it. This is one way, but it is usually more profitable to start a little further back. Presumably you knocked off your specimen from some exposure. Start with the exposure rather than the specimen. Rocks fall (roughly) into three classes: Sedimentary—those rocks that were laid down in water, or on land; Metamorphic—those rocks that, whatever their origin, have gone through great changes, altering their form and appearance; and Igneous—a wide group of rocks but having one thing in common, the fact that at some time they have been molten.

Some of the rocks from these three classes can be confused, one with another, in hand specimens. Their appearance in the field is mostly quite different. For this reason the practised geologist starts his observations on the exposure and determines what he would call its field relations. Does the rock occur in beds? The beds may be of any thickness, from a fraction of an inch to many feet. They may lie quite horizontally or they may slope. They may stand vertically on end, or be folded in anything from long sweeping folds to tiny puckers—*but they are bedded.* If the beds are regular and very thin it is most likely that they are of sedimentary origin. If the beds are thick, even very thick, they may still be sedimentary, but caution is needed for they might be lavas.

Bedded rocks suspected of being sedimentary should be carefully examined along the bedding planes for ripple marks, rainspotting, drying cracks or fossils. In the mass the beds may be parallel, but each separate bed may show current bedding. Any of these features can be taken as weighty evidence in favour of a sedimentary origin, but few of them would show very well on a small hand specimen. Ripple marking reveals that the sediment was laid down in water of no great depth. It also helps with identification further, for only rocks which contain a fair amount of sand will show ripple marks. Rain spots and sun cracks can only mean beds exposed at low water. Current bedding where the smaller beds run diagonally into one another while the larger beds are roughly parallel, suggests a deposit laid down in shallow water with strong currents which swept the sediment first one way and then the other. This kind of bedding is most frequent in sandstones. Should the beds be be predominantly red as well as current bedded, one should suspect desert conditions, and here the actual sand grains are sometimes beautifully rounded.

A careful scrutiny will often reveal fossils of some kind either in the rock or upon the bedding planes. Look for things like shells, crinoids, graptolites or trilobites. Fossils of any kind virtually settle the issue as to whether or not the rock is sedimentary. Fossils in rocks of igneous origin are so rare as to cause a great stir when found. If none of these things can be found, and if at the same time the beds are comparatively thick, you can postpone judgement. The beds may be lavas.

Now we can pay a little more attention to the rock in hand specimen. If the rock is obviously made up of fragments the character of these fragments should be carefully noted. Rounded pebbles cemented together form the rock *conglomerate* and tell of an ancient shoreline. Angular fragments cemented together give the rock known as *breccia,* and here one needs to be careful. Some breccias are indeed sedimentary, though they are not common in our district except in the case of the Brockram, which is almost always reddish in colour. Others may be of volcanic origin, and these we shall consider later.

The fragments of which the rock is made up may be quite small grains of sand in fact—or they may be so small as to be scarcely discernible, but they are grains. Bedded rocks composed of grains are most often of sedimentary origin. I have worked out a table of the bedded rocks which I trust may be of some assistance in distinguishing one rock from another.

I have not treated the metamorphic rocks in this way. Fortunately the rocks of this class which are likely to be met on these excursions are few and can be quickly dealt with. Around the Skiddaw Granite there are only three types and all are bedded. The chiastolite slate was originally a black mudstone to which the application of heat has brought marked changes. First the new mineral chiastolite has been formed from the clay minerals and secondly much of the carbon has been driven off leaving the

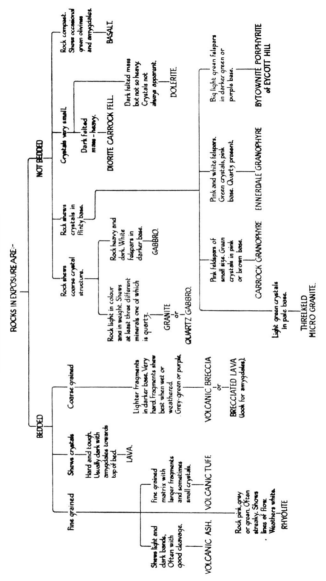

IDENTIFICATION OF ROCKS :- IGNEOUS

ROCKS IN EXPOSURE ARE :-

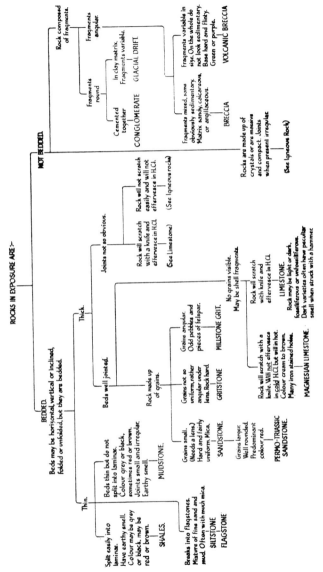

KEY TO THE IDENTIFICATION OF ROCKS

ROCKS IN EXPOSURE ARE :-

BEDDED.
Beds may be horizontal, vertical or inclined, folded or unfolded, but they are bedded.

NOT BEDDED.

Thin.

Split easily into laminae.
Have earthy smell.
Colour may be grey or black, may be red or brown.
SHALES.

Beds thin but do not split into laminae.
Colour grey or black, sometimes red or brown. Joints small and irregular. Earthy smell.
MUDSTONE.

Breaks into flagstones.
Mixture of fine sand and mud. Often with much mica.
SILTSTONE
FLAGSTONE

Thick.

Beds well jointed.

Rock made up of grains.

Grains small.
(Needs a lens.)
Hard and fairly uniform. Mica.
SANDSTONE.

Grains larger.
Well rounded.
Predominant colour red.
PERMO-TRIASSIC SANDSTONE.

Grains not so uniform, rather angular under lens. Rock hard.
GRITSTONE

Grains angular.
Odd pebbles and pieces of felspar.
MILLSTONE GRIT.

Joints not so obvious.

Rock will scratch with a knife and effervesce in HCl.
(See Limestone)

Rock will not scratch easily and will not effervesce in HCl.
(See Igneous rocks)

No grains visible.
May be shell fragments.

Rock will scratch with a knife and effervesce in HCl
LIMESTONE
Rock may be light or dark, fossiliferous or unfossiliferous. Dark varieties often have peculiar smell when struck with a hammer.

Rock will scratch with a knife. Will not effervesce in cold HCl but will in hot. Colour cream to brown. Many iron stained holes.
MAGNESIAN LIMESTONE.

Rock composed of fragments.

Fragments round.

Cemented together
CONGLOMERATE

In clay matrix.
Fragments variable.
GLACIAL DRIFT

Fragments angular.

Fragments variable in size. On the whole do not look sedimentary. Base hard and flinty. Green or purple.
VOLCANIC BRECCIA

Fragments mixed, some obviously sedimentary. Matrix sandy, calcareous, or argillaceous.
BRECCIA

Rocks are made up of crystals or are massive and compact. Joints when present irregular.
(See Igneous Rock)

rock rather grey in colour. The spotted slate was once a siltstone, or sandy mudstone, and the black dots are clots of iron sulphide, concentrated maybe by heat. The so-called mica-schist, or cordierite hornfels, was originally a muddy sandstone and is characterized by fine layers of mica with dark spots, some of which are cordierite. It is a hard rock, usually much contorted, and is found in close proximity to the Skiddaw Granite. Around the Shap Granite the most obvious rocks of metamorphic character are to be found in the Blue Rock Quarry and here the original rock was Borrowdale Volcanic. There are other rocks close to the Shap Granite which have been affected by heat, noticeably a Silurian Grit on Pack Horse Hill which has been changed to a quartzite. The Coniston Limestone is found in a highly metamorphosed condition west of Wasdale Head Farm with the production of many lime-bearing new minerals such as idocrase, tremolite and wollastonite.

The igneous rocks are many and variable. The granites and the gabbro of Carrock Fell are all noticeably blocky in appearance. Joints, often well marked but irregular, run through the rock. Any suggestion of bedding is purely coincidental and it does not take much experience to differentiate between these igneous and sedimentary rocks. On the other hand lavas and ashes can be well bedded, and indeed why not? The lavas were poured out as separate flows one above the other, while the ashes, tuffs and even the coarser breccias were accumulated bed above bed, some of them at least, under water. In any attempt to classify rocks of this kind we must remember that we are on difficult ground and should look beyond their appearance in the mass. Here the texture of the rock is of most help but, unfortunately, this often calls for the aid of a microscope and thin rock section. I have tried to work out a scheme of identification which I trust may be a help, from it you should be able to spot at least some of the more obvious ones; should some of the others puzzle you you can console yourself with the reflection that you are in good company—they often puzzle experienced geologists too!

A few pointers may be of help. Lavas, being tougher than ashes, stand the weather better, and as a result form the steep ground. The ashes give the more gentle ground between. Lavas almost invariably somewhere show steam holes and these should be sought, while the jointing of lavas is generally better developed than in the ashes. Ashes on the other hand often show their fragmental character and take on cleavage better than the lavas. A total absence of steam holes does not prove a rock is not a lava, but it is a good pointer.

I wish I could say with honesty that I can always sort out lavas and ashes in the field with ease. Alas, it is not so. I often find it necessary to have a thin section before I can be certain.

17. Identification of Minerals

THE identification of minerals by the beginner is not easy. It is not made easier by the fact that in and around Lakeland there are at least 120 different varieties. If at first you have to admit defeat and must seek help from someone rather more skilled, do not allow this to discourage you. With every successful identification the chance of further success becomes progressively greater. Experience is required, and this is born of doing things rather than sitting at the fireside reading about them.

I do not propose to deal with the rare minerals unless they can be identified fairly readily by the beginner. The fact that your find cannot be recognised from the following pages does not mean that it is valueless. Indeed you may have found something quite rare and valuable, for the luck of the beginner is proverbial!

One or two generalisations should be noted. In Lakeland, mineral veins have two predominant directions. Either they run north and south, or very nearly so, or they run roughly east and west. Generally speaking the north and south veins carry either lead or iron, while the east-west veins carry mostly copper. Zinc goes with lead as a rule, and some of the iron veins carry arsenic or tungsten. From each type of course there is a suite of derived or secondary minerals. From lead, for instance, you have cerussite or pyromorphite, and from copper, minerals like the lovely carbonates, malachite and azurite.

To recognise the type of vein under consideration is a distinct help, for it reduces the probabilities. Where things get really complicated are places where the two systems intersect each other. These intersections are, from the miner's point of view, most profitable. It is as well to remember that when a miner talks about the "run of a vein" he is referring to the magnetic bearing, not the true bearing.

On finding a mineral specimen, make an attempt to identify it from what you have read, for there is nothing quite like the thrill of a first find. Should you be puzzled, do not spend too much time on it. Remember that you can only collect in the field, and at first it is more important to arrive home with something to work upon than to identify there and then. If you are not sure, take a wrapping paper, write upon it what you think you have found and, most important, where it was found, and tuck your specimen away in your rucksack.

Forgive me if I seem a little tiresome in reverting again and again to this theme of making sure you know from where the specimens have come, but there is much sound sense in it. It can save time. It may be weeks later, possibly not until the winter months, that you bring out your finds for identification. If at this point you have no idea where they came from a lot of interest is gone. More important is the fact that some localities have a definite suite of minerals. A brownish mineral found at the old Force Crag Mines in Coledale is most likely to be zinc blende, while a mineral that, to the untrained eye, looks very similar but was found at Brandy Ghyll is far more likely to be wolfram. If, with beginner's luck you have stumbled across a rare and important find, it will be annoying both to yourself and to the expert who identifies it if you cannot recall its source!

John Postlethwaite, in his well-known *Mines and Mining in the Lake District,* gave a list of minerals and their localities. One of them, of great scientific interest, is the mineral stolzite, which he says came from Force Crag in Coledale. I have myself known stolzite and the locality given from the days when the mines were working, but although I have searched diligently I have never found stolzite, nor do I know any other collector who has. The obvious place to look for this mineral is Brandy Ghyll, for it is a tungstate of lead; there I and others have found it. Did our old friend Postlethwaite slip up on his locality? There is now no means of knowing but what we do know, and did not know until recent years, is that there is in the Coledale Fell area a hidden mass of granite. Is it an offshoot of the Skiddaw granite? We do not know for certain, but the idea is possible. We do know that stolzite is found quite close to where this granite and its greisen crops out. Did John Postlethwaite have a stroke of luck that no one else has repeated? Or did he unfortunately mix up his localities? If there is granite in the vicinity of Force Crag might there not also be tungstates? (Recently specimens of Apatite from the old Cobalt Mine on Scar Craggs have been claimed as identical, by X-ray spectograph, with Apatite from Brandy Ghyll).

A visit to a good museum is always worthwhile for mineral recognition and there are quite good collections both in Keswick and Carlisle. All the collectors I know are very, very human and they like to display the finest specimens they can get. These, moreover, have been carefully preserved. Please do not expect to find anything quite so grand lying around on a mine tip! I once came across a young student up at Brandy Ghyll who complained that he could not find galena although he had been told there were veins of it. He was most indignant when it was pointed out that he was sitting on the stuff. Galena, he assured me, was quite unmistakable; bright and silvery! So it is, in a museum, but not when it has been lying on a mine tip for the best part of a century. On a tip it is far more likely to be a dirty grey, or almost black. The only clue to suggest that it is anything out of the ordinary is its weight. The colour of weathered minerals is something the expert has learned from long experience but he is usually interested in a fresh fracture also.

What distinguishes one mineral from another? Fundamentally their chemical make-up is different but, apart from some simple tests which I will give, this is not easy to check. How are we to come to a decision? By carefully taking note of a number of ways in which each differs from the others even when at first sight they are similar. They vary in appearance, colour, crystal form, hardness and specific gravity. Beyond this many minerals behave quite differently when struck with a hammer. Some break always with a smooth bright surface, and this we call cleavage.

Of these many differences I suppose most beginners would rely on colour but this can be misleading as the same mineral can have many colours. If you take a piece of unglazed white pot, or a piece of fine white sandstone, and rub your mineral on this you will get a colour usually referred to as the "streak" and this is a far more reliable guide than apparent colour. Streak can be used as an aid to identification and where distinctive will be given. Crystal form can be a help should you be lucky enough to find a crystallized specimen.

This leaves hardness, specific gravity and fracture, and the first two of these can be particularly useful. Hardness is a relative thing and thus needs some comparative scale. Such a scale was suggested long ago by a mineralogist called Moh; it is made up from pieces of different minerals and runs thus:

Hardness	Mineral	Hardness	Mineral
1	Talc	6	Orthoclase
2	Gypsum	7	Quartz
3	Calcite	8	Topaz
4	Fluorspar	9	Corundum
5	Apatite	10	Diamond

The first thing to notice about this scale is that it is a comparative scale only. It must not be taken to imply that the hardness goes up by a constant increment. Diamond, for instance, is many times harder than corundum, but quartz, while definitely harder than orthoclase, is not all that much harder.

This scale, made up in a small tin box and with the specimens clearly numbered, can be bought for about £1·25. It is not too big or heavy and could be carried with you in the field, but there is the constant risk of loss and, on the whole, I think it is better kept at home. In the field one must compromise by relying on what can be easily carried; a knife, a brass pin or a copper coin. Finger nails are sometimes useful implements. With a little practice these humble tools can be made to yield a surprising amount of information. Using the key opposite a useful guide to mineral hardness can be obtained.

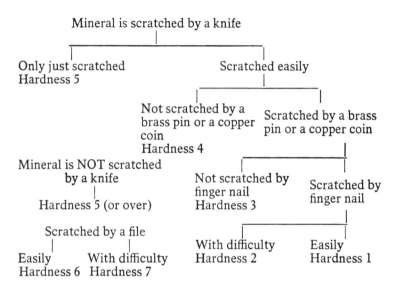

This looks simple enough, but a word of caution. In making a test for hardness it is necessary to be quite sure what scratches what. The scratch may be quite genuine, when for instance, it is made by the knife cutting into the specimen. It may be a mark left on the mineral by the knife, the metal of the knife having come off upon the mineral because the mineral is harder than the steel. A little experience soon teaches what is required.

Let us consider comparative weight or specific gravity. Technically the specific gravity of any substance is the weight of that substance compared with the weight of an equal volume of water. This is obviously not an easy proposition in the field, yet by "hefting" specimens in the hand one can soon learn to distinguish heavy minerals from light ones. A piece of quartz of similar size is a good guide. If this is as much as can be done outside, at home the problem is not so difficult. With a light spring balance of the laboratory type such as can be bought quite cheaply, a piece of fine silk thread, and a glass of water, one can make a reasonably accurate determination.

In making such specific gravity checks, choose a piece of mineral that is all mineral—as free as possible from veinstone. Try and avoid small holes. Should the specimen be part mineral and part quartz your determination will obviously be inaccurate. Should the specimen have small holes in it these will hold tiny bubbles of air, and this will affect your result.

Attach a good specimen by the silk thread to the balance and carefully note the reading. Then with the specimen still attached to the balance submerge it completely in water making sure there are no clinging bubbles of air (just a drop of detergent will help with this). Taking a second reading it will be found that the mineral now appears to weigh less than it did before. Note this second reading, and by substituting your readings in this formula the specific gravity is readily obtained:

$$\frac{\text{Weight in air}}{\text{Weight in air} - \text{apparent weight in water}} = \text{Specific Gravity}$$

If you like to get things as close as possible, and you have sufficient material, take three pieces which meet the requirements. Make three determinations and average the results. Should any one of your results be widely different, there is something wrong, either with your technique or one of your specimens.

Not all minerals are found crystallized. Those that are, even where a crystal form is not apparent, usually break in a definite way when struck with a hammer. This is called cleavage and the phenomenon is due to planes of weakness in the crystal structure. Galena will yield little cubes, while calcite cleaves into rhombs which look like elongated cubes pushed over sideways. This test is not applied to beautifully crystallized specimens! Even amorphous minerals often have markedly different ways of breaking and this can be used as an aid to identification; this is called fracture.

Without the full resources of a laboratory and the requisite chemical training, a thorough-going analysis is out of the question. There are a few tests which, although dependent on the chemical composition, can be readily applied. One of these is the flame test. To make such a test you require a thin piece of platinum wire about three inches long, some dilute hydrochloric acid and a bunsen burner. Usually the wire is sealed into a piece of glass tubing for easy handling and this is easy enough to do. Simply heat the wire and the end of the tube in a bunsen flame until both are white hot and then introduce the tip of the wire into the melting glass. When the two have cooled the wire will be firmly fixed into the end of the tube. The first requisite is to make absolutely sure the wire is clean. To do this place a few drops of hydrochloric acid in a watch glass or saucer; heat the wire to a white heat, dip it again into HCl and reheat. Do this until no coloration of the flame is visible. *Never*, under any circumstances, introduce the wire direct into the acid bottle.

Having cleaned the wire you are now ready to make a test. Place a small amount of the crushed mineral upon a watch glass or a clean piece of paper, adjust the bunsen until the flame is colourless and then, moistening the wire with *clean* acid, pick up a little powdered mineral and introduce it into the flame. You may need to repeat this once or twice, watching carefully, for some of the colours are very short lived.

Colour of Flame	Indicates
Brick Red	Calcium
Purplish Red	Lithium
Crimson	Strontium
Yellow	Sodium
Apple Green	Barium
Yellowish Green	Molybdenum
Blue Green	Zinc
Greyish blue	Antimony
Pale sky blue	Lead, or Arsenic
Strong sky blue	Copper
Lilac	Potassium

The most difficult of these is probably potassium. The lilac flame of potassium is so easily masked by other colours, particularly by sodium. The only way round this is to observe the flame through a piece of very dark blue glass—arc welder's goggles, for instance.

Another very useful test is the borax bead. On the end of the platinum wire form a small loop around the tip of a pencil (about 1/8th of an inch). Heat the wire and dip it into pure borax. Introducing this into the flame will cause the borax to melt. Should the loop not be filled repeat until you have, on cooling, a colourless bead. As distinctly different beads are given by the *same* mineral, depending upon the kind of flame you use, make sure that you have an oxidising flame for your first tests. To get this flame adjust the bunsen until all the yellow has gone from the flame and it is blue or colourless. Now heat the bead and while it is soft pick up a tiny fragment of the powdered mineral and then reheat. Remembering that not all minerals will react, watch your bead carefully. If it appears to bubble and boil and your fragment slowly disappears this augurs well. When the agitation has subsided remove the bead and carefully observe its colour while hot and its colour when cold.

If no colour is observed repeat the process, picking up another small fragment. This may be slow but it is much more likely to be successful than swamping your bead with mineral. If you do this you will get an opaque bead that tells you nothing. Whether you have met with success, or appear to have failed, get rid of the bead by heating and flicking it out of the loop. Now very carefully clean the wire until even the yellow sodium of the borax is gone. Making another bead. adjust your flame to a yellow (reducing) flame and proceed as before. Check your results against this table.

Oxidising Flame	Reducing Flame	Indication
Deep Blue	Deep Blue	Cobalt
Green—hot Sky blue—cold }	Red—hot } Opaque—cold }	Copper
Reddish—hot Yellowy green—cold }	Emerald green	Chromium
Reddish brown—hot Yellow—cold }	Greenish	Iron
Reddish violet—hot Amethystine—cold }	Colourless	Manganese
Colourless—hot Colourless or opaque }		Silica, calcium, or zinc

These tests are fairly simple and, apart from the platinum wire, inexpensive, but they do need practice. One good way to begin is by experimenting with known substances. i.e. chemicals, either from the laboratory or by buying from the chemist. A word of caution: If you have any reason to suspect lead or arsenic use as little of your wire as possible, for with these two elements the platinum will react, turning grey and brittle, and tending to break off.

We now have a variety of tests which can be applied to help in checking any mineral specimen. These are hardness, specific gravity, fracture and/or cleavage, besides the simple chemical tests outlined above. This leaves colour, the colour as seen, the more reliable streak and finally, if we are in luck, crystal form.

The identification of minerals now becomes rather like a detective story. You are the detective and. totting up the various clues derived from your examination, you can arrive at a decision. It is best to follow a fixed plan when dealing with the unknown. Short cuts as often as not lead only to wrong determinations. First find the hardness by finding the mineral from your test set that will just scratch your specimen and the one that is just scratched by the specimen. Next ascertain as nearly as possible the specific gravity. Notice the way in which the mineral fractures, paying particular attention to any cleavage. Try flame and then borax bead tests, and do not forget streak. Having made a note of all these look down the list of minerals arranged by colour and see which of them comes nearest to your tests.

MINERAL LISTS

WHITE OR COLOURLESS MINERALS

The mineral is found massive or granular. Rarely stalactitic. Crystals not uncommon, especially in veins or in vugs in granite. The purer the mineral the more colourless and glass-like it tends to become. Crystals take the form of hexagonal prisms or pyramids, or combinations of the two. H. 7. Sp.Gr. 2.65. Fracture irregular. Cleavage none. B.B. Opaque. Streak difficult to determine but whitish.
As a veinstone and as grains in sandstone one of the commonest of mins.
QUARTZ. SiO_2.

*   *   *

The mineral is white or colourless (occasionally tinged by other mins.). Transparent to opaque. Found massive, fibrous or stalactitic. Crystals are very common but most variable in form.
H. 3. O Sp.Gr. 2.71. Cleavage perfect. Rhombohedral. Powder made up of tiny rhombs. Fl.T. Brick Red. Streak. White.
Not uncommon as a veinstone. Chief constituent of limestones. Very pure transparent form showing double refraction. "Iceland Spar."
CALCITE. $CaCO_2$.

*   *   *

The mineral is white to creamy. Occasionally colourless. Usually opaque but can be translucent or transparent.
Found commonly as a veinstone, massive, compact or in tabular crystals. Sensibly heavy.
H.2.5—3.5. Sp.Gr. 4.5. Cleavage perfect in three directions. Fl. T. apple green. Streak white.
In Lakeland proper the mineral is usually opaque, if crystallized generally tabular. The transparent variety is more common on the Alston Block. There are fine veins at Force Crag and near Caldbeck.
BARYTES, or HEAVY SPAR. $BaSO_4$.

*   *   *

The mineral is white, grey or colourless. Occurs massive or compact but more usually as prismatic crystals. Often radiating or cruciform. H.3.0. Sp.Gr. 6.46—6.48. Fracture. Very brittle. Fl. T. Pale sky blue. Streak white.
Fairly common in the weathered part of lead veins as at the Barrow and Blencathra mines.
CERUSSITE. $PbCO_3$.

*   *   *

The mineral is white or greyish white. Occasionally colourless. Often shows a vitreous to pearly lustre. Usually occurs as lath-like crystals in acid igneous rocks. Sometimes found massive.
H. 6.0. Sp.Gr. 2.57. Cleavage good. Two planes at right angles, smooth and shiny. Fl. T. Lilac (but only with difficulty) B.B. A transparent glass. Streak white. Turned about in a good light often shows a twin plane down the length of the crystal.
Common in the Shap Granite and in vugs in the rock (here shaded pink).
ORTHOCLASE FELSPAR. $KAl.Si_3.O_8$.

*   *   *

Mineral is white, greyish or tinged red. Also colourless.
Often in tabular crystals showing many twin planes if turned in a good light. Has a vitreous to pearly look, especially on cleavage planes.
H. 6.0—6.5. Sp.Gr. 2.62—2.64. Cleavage good. Two planes but at less than the right angle. Fl. T. Indifferent. Depends on composition. Streak white to colourless. Can be massive but usually as lath-like

crystals in intermediate or basic rocks. The Gabbro of Carrock Fell.
PLAGIOCLASE FELSPAR. Complex Aluminium Silicates.

*   *   *

The mineral is found in white to silvery flakes. Sometimes tinged yellow
or brownish. Often shows hexagonal forms. More or less pearly.
Transparent to Translucent.
H. 2.0—2.5. Sp. Gr. 2.85. Cleavage extremely perfect into easily separable
laminae which are flexible. Streak whitish.
A common mineral in granites.
MUSCOVITE MICA. $3H_2O.K_2O.3$
$A_2O_3.6SiO_2$.
The variety found on the greisen at Brandy Ghyll is known as
GILBERTITE.

*   *   *

The mineral is found as four sided pyramids and is colourless. Has a
vitreous look.
H.4.5—5.0. Sp.Gr. 5.9—6.1. Fracture uneven, brittle. Shows some
cleavage. B.B. Blue in the reducing flame. Streak white.
Found with other minerals at Brandy Ghyll. Occasionally with wolfram
more commonly with Mispickel. These crystals, always small, are
becoming rare.
SCHEELITE. $CaWO_4$.

GREEN MINERALS

The mineral is a bright green. If massive will probably be botryoidal in
form and show a banded arrangement with different shades of green.
Often found encrusting, granular or earthy.
H.3.5—4.0. Sp.Gr. 3.7—4.0. Lustre silky. Flame test. Strong sky blue
B.Bead.O.F. sky blue, cold. Streak paler than the mineral. Will
dissolve with effervescence in cold HCl forming a blue-green
solution. Encrusting fairly common. Massive not so common on
tips. Crystals rare anywhere. Newlands and Roughtenghyll.
MALACHITE. $CuCO_3. Cu(OH)_2$.

*   *   *

The mineral is green but has a dull flat look. Occurs as incrustations or
in thin seams. If massive or botryoidal often with an enamel-like surface.
H.2.0—4.0, Sp.Gr. 2.0—2.3. Both varying with composition.
Fracture conchoidal. Sometimes sectile. Fl.T. Sky blue.
B.Bead. Sky blue. Streak white.
Can be mistaken for malachite but does not react with HCl except
to slowly decompose.
Of common occurrence along with copper minerals. Caldbeck Fells.
CHRYSOCOLLA. While the composition varies it is essentially
$CuO.SiO_2.2H_2O$.

*   *   *

The mineral is emerald green to a blackish green. If massive, shows a
reniform structure. more usually either encrusting or as small prismatic
crystals.
H.3.5—4.0. Sp.Gr. 3.9. Fracture uneven. Cleavage good with a pearly
surface. Fl.T. Bright sky blue. B.B. Sky blue. Streak a paler green.
Found with other copper minerals at Roughtenghyll but not too
common.
BROCHANTITE. $CuSO_4. 3Cu(OH)_2$.
The mineral is green or yellowish green (sometimes flecked with brown).
Has a resinous look. Often as prismatic crystals and aggregated to form
crusts. Sometimes reniform or botryoidal. Also encrusting.

H.3.5—4.0. Sp.Gr. 6.5—7.1. Fracture uneven and brittle. Fl.T. Pale sky blue. Streak white. Found commonly with lead ores in the Caldbeck Fells. Fairly common around Driggeth Mine.
PYROMORPHITE or Green Lead Ore. $3Pb_3.P_2O_8PbCl_2$.

* * *

The mineral is green but of various shades. Occasionally white or colourless. Usually found as six sided prisms, sometimes with pyramidal ends. Lustre sub-resinous to vitreous.
H.5.0 Sp.Gr. 3.17—3.23. Cleavage poor. Fl.T. Brick red. Streak white. Found not uncommonly as small crystals in quartz at Brandy Ghyll. Also as an accessory mineral in igneous rocks.
APATITE. Composition variable with two main varieties.
Fluor-apatite. $3Ca_3P_2O_8.CaF_2$.
Chlor-apatite. $3Ca_3P_2O_8.CaCl_2$.

* * *

The mineral is pistachio green to a dark oily green. Occurs as six sided crystals but often wider along one axis. Sometimes as aggregates and vein fillings.
H.6.0—7.0. Sp.Gr. 3.25—3.5. Fracture uneven. Cleavage good on one plane. B.B. Ox. Fl. yellow. Red. Fl. green. Streak greyish, colourless. Not uncommon as small crystals in the Blue Rock Quarry, Shap. Sometimes as crystals in vugs in the B.V.S. more often as veins and disseminations. Lavas of Walla Crag.
EPIDOTE. $Ca_2(Al,Fe), (OH) (SiO_4)_3$.

* * *

The mineral is a pale green to grey-green. Massive, reniform, botryoidal or encrusting. When massive often shows banding. Vitreous inclining to pearly. Translucent to opaque.
H.5.0. Sp.Gr. 4.0—4.5. Often shows good cleavage. Fl.T. and B. Beads are rather poor. Dissolves in HCl. with effervescence. Found at Roughtenghyll sparingly.
CALAMINE. (The Smithsonite of the Americans.) $ZnCO_3$.

BLACK MINERALS

The mineral is black or a greyish black. Massive or as shiny blades in white quartz. Sensibly heavy. Crystals are tabular but uncommon.
H.5.0—5.5. Sp.Gr. 7.1—7.9. Fracture uneven. Shows one perfect cleavage. Cleavage planes sub-metallic, black and shining whereas fractures are dull. B.B. Green in Red. F. Streak Chocolate brown. Found in the tips at Brandy Ghyll.
WOLFRAM. $(Fe,Mn) WO_4$.

* * *

The mineral is black to brownish-black. Sometimes yellowish. Has a resinous look but can be adamantine.
H.3.5—4.0. Sp.Gr. 3.9—4.2. Cleavage good with planes bright and shiny. Fracture rough and brittle. Streak white to brown. Crystals are quite common but the crystal form is often complex due to twinning. On the tips at Force Crag.
ZINC BLENDE or SPHALERITE. ZnS. (The miner's "Black Jack".)

* * *

The mineral is iron black and shiny. Found as irregular grains or as octahedra in Gabbro.
H.5.5—6.5. Sp.Gr. 4.9—5.2. B.B. O.Fl. colourless. Red. Fl. Bottle green. Streak black. Soluble in HCl. Grains attracted by a magnet.
MAGNETITE. Fe_3O_4.

* * *

The mineral is black or greenish black. Usually opaque. Occurs as bundles of needles. Often radiating. Good crystals are six sided. H.7.0—7.5. Sp.Gr. 2.98—3.2. Fracture uneven. Streak white. A mineral of pneumotolysis. Found in Poddy Ghyll. Carrock Fell, and in both the Threlkeld Micro-granite and in the Eskdale Granite. SCHORL. A variety of Tourmaline. A complex boro-silicate.

*　　*　　*

The mineral is most commonly black, deep brown or dark green. Occurs as flakes which are sometimes pseudo-hexagonal. H.2.5—3.0. Sp.Gr. 2.7—3.1. Cleavage very perfect yielding extremely thin flexible and elastic laminae. Lustre splendent, on cleavage faces tends to pearly. Found commonly in rocks like granite, diorite, gabbro etc. BIOTITE. There are a number of varieties so composition varies but all are complex hydrated silicates of potassium, magnesium and iron.

*　　*　　*

The mineral is found as scales or mica-like rhombohedral crystals. Black, metallic and resplendent. Occasionally as rosettes. Generally in association with haematite. H.5.5. Sp.Gr. 4.5—5.3. B.B. Ox. Fl. yellow. Red. Fl. Green. Streak cherry red. Most commonly in vugs and with quartz in the iron mines of Cumberland and Furness. SPECULAR ORE. Fe_2O_3.

*　　*　　*

The mineral is iron black passing into dark steel grey. Found massive botryodial and stalactitic. H. Variable 5.0—7.0. Sp.Gr. 3.3—4.7. Lustre submetallic or dull. B.B. Ox. Fl. Amethystine. Red Fl. Colourless. Streak a brownish black, shining. An opaque mineral. PSILOMELANE. A manganese oxide with impurities. Found fairly commonly at Force Crag.

GREY MINERALS

The mineral is a steel grey to tin white (fresh fracture). Tarnishes readily to a pale coppery colour. Crystals, which are not uncommon, are flat and tabular often showing the fine lines of crystal growth. H.5.5—6.0. Sp.Gr. 6.1. Fracture uneven and brittle. Sparks when struck with a hammer and emits a pungent smell of garlic. Streak is a greyish black. Found in the tips at Brandy Ghyll. MISPICKEL or ARSENICAL PYRITES. Fe.AsS.

*　　*　　*

The mineral is lead grey to almost black, but silvery if freshly fractured. Crystals, which are not rare, are either modified cubes or sometimes simple cubes. Also found massive and granular. H.2.5. Sp.Gr. 7.2—7.7. Fracture. Flat, even, or tends to conchoidal. Cleavage is perfect and cubic. Most specimens will break into little cubes when struck. Streak black. A common mineral in Lakeland. GALENA. PbS. The "blue ore" of miners.

*　　*　　*

The mineral is grey to a steel grey. Found in scales, laminae or in small pieces. Sometimes earthy. Very soft and cold to the touch. Sectile and opaque. H.1.0—2.0. Sp.Gr. 2.0—2.3 (depending on purity). Streak black and shiny. Not a common mineral. In Lakeland found only at Seathwaite in Borrowdale and very sparingly in Bannerdale. Could be mistaken for molybdenite but the streak here is a greeny-black. GRAPHITE or PLUMBAGO. Pure Carbon.

*　　*　　*

The mineral is grey to dark steel grey. Massive or reniform. Sometimes with a fibrous or radiating structure. Usually soils the fingers. H.2.0—2.5. Sp.Gr. 4.8. Fracture rather brittle. B.B. Ox. Fl. amethyst. Red Fl. colourless. Found at mines in Calbeck Fells.
PYROLUSITE. MnO_2.

*   *   *

The mineral is a grey to bluish grey. Reniform or massive. Can show a fine radiating structure. Crystals very rare. H.5.5—6.5. Sp.Gr. 4.5—5.3. Fracture uneven. Cleavage poor. B.B. for iron. Streak cherry red. On weathered surfaces shades of red when the mineral soils the fingers. The red colour along many of Lakeland's shatter belts is due to this mineral. Common in West Cumberland, Eskdale etc.
HAEMATITE. Fe_2O_3.

*   *   *

The mineral is a lead grey tending to a tin white, sometimes with a yellowy tarnish. Specimens small, foliated or fibrous. H.2.0. Sp.Gr. 6.4—6.5. Lustre metallic. Cleaves into thin leaves. Streak, grey. Found fairly commonly at Brandy Ghyll on quartz and on the joints in Shap Granite.
BISMUTHINITE. Bi_2S_3.
There is a variety answering to this description found at Brandy Ghyll but the cleavage planes are mirror bright. This is the very rare mineral Joseite, a telluride of bismuth.

*   *   *

The mineral is lead grey with a bluish cast. Sometimes rather silvery. H.1.5. Sp.Gr. 4.4—4.8. Easily scratched by the finger nail. Sectile. Cleavage perfect into flexible laminae. Metallic lustre. Streak greenish black. Fairly common in scales of foliated clumps both at Brandy Ghyll and at Shap.
MOLYBDENITE. MoS_2.

*   *   *

The mineral occurs as sizeable grey-green crystals in a lava. May show as six-sided end sections, more commonly rectangular, lath-like. H.5.0—6.0. Sp.Gr. 2.6—2.75. Fracture rough. Cleavage good. Two planes less than a right angle, pearly. Streak white. One twin plane, as a rule, by reflected light although the mineral is in fact multiply twinned. A rare mineral but well seen at Linewath Bridge, Eycott Hill.
BYTOWNITE. A plagioclase felspar.

BROWN MINERALS

The mineral shows shades of brown on fracture. Yellowish brown to yellow when earthy. The mammillated and stalactitic forms usually have a black glazed coating. Often radiating or fibrous. H.5.0—5.5. Sp.Gr. 3.6—4.0. B.B. Iron reactions. Streak. Yellowish brown. A hydrated form of haematite. Not an uncommon mineral particularly in the iron mines of West Cumberland.
LIMONITE. $2Fe_2O_3.3H_2O$.

*   *   *

The mineral is brown. Looks metallic and is sensibly heavy. Crystals tabular but more commonly massive or bladed. H.5.0—5.5. Sp.Gr. 7.1—7.9. Fracture uneven. Cleavage good with the cleavage planes black rather than brown. B.B. for iron. Streak a chocolate brown. Common at Brandy Ghyll where specimens can be found by digging in the tips.
WOLFRAM. $(Fe,Mn) WO_4$.

*   *

The mineral is brown or almost black. Resinous to adamantine. Crystals, which are fairly common and belong to the cubic system, are resplendent when fresh. Otherwise dull.
H.3.5—4.0. Sp.Gr. 3.9—4.2. Cleavage good, bright and shiny. Streak white or brown. Soluble in HCl. Found at Force Crag, Thornthwaite etc.
ZINC BLENDE or SPHALERITE. ZnS.

* * *

The mineral is dark brown or greeny brown. Commonly as crystals which are rhombic, or as brown patches.
H. Varies, but usually 7 or over. Sp.Gr. About 3.8. Lustre vitreous. Common in the green rock quarry at Shap where the best crystals are found in the calcite stringers.
GARNET. Largely Andradite, although all garnets are mixtures.

RED MINERALS

The mineral is red in colour. Feels greasy and soils the fingers. When freshly broken may still be red but is then more often a bluish grey.
H.5.0—6.5. Sp.Gr. 4.0—5.3. Fracture depends on the type of ore. Rough in the softer kinds to splintery in the harder, fibrous types. B.B. Iron reactions. Streak always a cherry red. Common in the mines of West Cumberland and in veins in Lakeland, Eskdale, Langdale etc.
HAEMATITE. Fe_2O_3.

* * *

The mineral occurs as globules or as many sided crystals. In colour a deep red to purplish.
H.6.5—7.5. Sp.Gr. 3.9—4.2. Fracture uneven. Lustre vitreous. Common in the rocks of the Borrowdale Volcanic Series. Good localities are Illgill Head and Gt. Gable.
ALMADINE. If well crystallized and transparent—precious garnet.

* * *

The mineral occurs as a pulverulent coating on lead ores. A vivid red in colour.
H.2.0—3.0. Sp.Gr. 4.6. Lustre dull. Opaque. Streak orange yellow. A rare mineral this, and while it has been found in Lakeland it is more common in the Alston mines.
MINIMUM or RED LEAD ORE. Pb_3O_4.

BLUE MINERALS

The mineral is a deep azure blue. Found mostly as an incrustation, rarely massive, and crystals in Lakeland are doubtful. In fact it is not a common mineral with us.
H.3.5—4.25. Sp.Gr. 3.5—3.8. Fl.T. Sky blue. B.B. for copper. Streak a lighter blue than the mineral. Dissolves in HCl with effervescence giving a blue-green solution. Found sparingly at Dalehead, at Yewthwaite and the Goldscope.
AZURITE or CHESSYLITE. $2CuCO_3.Cu(OH)_2$.

* * *

The mineral is a deep azure blue. Usually shows platy crystals.
H.3.0—3.5. Sp.Gr. 5.4. Fracture brittle. Cleavage good. Flame tests and borax beads give poor copper reactions. Streak pale blue. Normally a very rare mineral but not uncommon around Roughtenghyll and Redghyll. Often mistaken for Azurite.
LINARITE. A complex lead-copper sulphate.

* * *

The mineral is a lovely sky blue to pale blue-green. Found in drusy incrustations.

H. ? Sp.Gr. 3.6. Lustre pearly. Gives copper reactions. Found sparingly around Roughtenghyll.
AURICHALCITE. A basic carbonate of zinc and copper.

*   *   *

The mineral is a light blue, mammillated or encrusting. Sometimes shows blue and white banding. Also as tiny crystals in vugs.
H.4.5—5.0. Sp.Gr. 3.1—3.5. Fracture brittle and uneven. Lustre vitreous to pearly. Streak white. Gelatinises in acids. Found sparingly at Roughtenghyll.
HEMIMORPHITE. (Calamine of the Americans.) $H_2O.2ZnO\ SiO_2$.

YELLOW MINERALS

The mineral is a pale brass to bronze yellow. May be massive but is quite commonly found as crystals, either as cubes or modified cubes. Faces of cubes often striated with the stria on adjacent faces at right angles.
H.6.0—6.5. Sp.Gr. 4.8—5.1. Fracture brittle and conchoidal. Lustre metallic and splendent. Sparks when struck with a hammer. B.B. iron reactions. Streak a greenish black. A very common mineral. Well seen on the joint faces in the Shap Quarry.
IRON PYRITES. Mundic Ore. "Fool's gold". FeS.

*   *   *

The mineral is a brass yellow. Frequently tarnished and sometimes iridescent. Usually found massive. Crystals when found appear to be cubic but are really tetragonal.
H.3.5—4.0. Sp.Gr. 4.1—4.3. (Compare with pyrites.) Fracture uneven. Lustre metallic but opaque. Does not spark when struck. B.B. Rather indifferent. Can give copper or iron reactions. Streak greenish black. Not uncommon in Newlands and at Coniston.
CHALCOPYRITES or COPPER PYRITES. $Cu_2S.Fe_2S_3$.

*   *   *

The mineral is yellow to greenish yellow. Has a resinous look and is sensibly heavy. Encrusting, massive, or in small hexagonal prisms.
H.3.5—4.0. Sp.Gr. 6.5—7.0. Cleavage poor. Fl.T. Pale sky blue. Streak white to yellowish white. Fairly common in the Caldbeck Fells.
PYROMORPHITE. $3Pb_3(PO_4)_2PbCl_2$.

*   *   *

The mineral is golden-yellow to a brownish-yellow and occurs in small barrel-like crystals. Sometimes in crusts.
H.3.5. Sp.Gr. 7.21. Fracture uneven, brittle. Cleavage poor. Lustre resinous. Streak white or nearly so. Found on the tips in Drygill. Once quite common, now one needs to dig.
CAMPYLITE. A Lakeland variety of Mimetite. An arsenate of lead with about 3% of phosphorus.

*   *   *

The mineral occurs as minute yellow flakes with a waxy look on a green incrustation.
H.2.75. Sp.Gr. 6.7—7.0 (but both would be difficult to determine). A very rare mineral, found on the centre tip in upper Brandy Ghyll.
WULFENITE. $PbMoO_4$.

*   *   *

The mineral is a pale to brownish yellow, looks resinous and is noticeably heavy.
H.4.5—5.0. Sp.Gr. 5.9—6.1. Fracture uneven. Cleavage good. Lustre vitreous to adamantine. Transparent to translucent. Found alone or with other minerals, most commony mispickel, at Brandy Ghyll.
SCHEELITE. $CaWO_4$.

Glossary of Geological Terms

Acid rocks. A term applied to rocks of igneous origin with a high silica content. Rocks with over 66% silica usually contain free quartz. Granite is a deep-seated rock of this character, while a rhyolite is an extrusive example.

Adit. A mine working driven into the hillside. Sometimes called a "level", but in fact they are usually driven off level to give natural drainage.

Agglomerate. A volcanic rock of explosive origin characterised by sharp angular fragments in a base of fine volcanic dust. Often contains pieces of rock through which the explosion took place, i.e. Skiddaw Slate in the purple breccia, which is an agglomerate.

Alpine. Pertaining to the Alps. In geological parlance refers to the series of mountain-building movements that built the Alps (along with most other present day mountain chains) or to the time when these movements took place, i.e. Lower tertiary times.

Amygdale. An almond. Refers to the steam holes in lava often filled with light-coloured secondary minerals. The minerals themselves are very variable, agate, calcite, chlorite being common whilst the zeolites are not so common in Lakeland.

Andesite. A lava. So called from the Andes of South America, where rocks of this kind were first studied. Intermediate between rhyolite and basalt. Its silica content ranges from 55 to 66%. The felspars are usually plagioclase, with either augite or enstatite. Free quartz is rare; an andesite with free quartz is called a dacite. A large proportion of the Borrowdale lavas are andesitic.

Anhydrite. A mineral of the evaporite group. Anhydrous calcium sulphate.

Anticline. Beds of rock forced up into the form of an arch.

Ash. An old term; more specifically—a volcanic ash. Refers to fragments blown from a present-day crater or to such fragments cemented into a rock. Today referred to as Tuff.

Augite. A pyroxene (q.v.). A complex mineral of rather variable composition, a silicate of magnesium, iron and aluminium. Usually seen as stumpy crystals, black or greeny-black in colour, in basic rocks like basalt, gabbros, dolerite, and some andesites.

Base Line. Or more fully "base line of erosion". The profile of erosion plotted along a river's course from its source to the sea. The Thalweg.
The sea level is the ultimate base beneath which a river cannot cut, but temporary bases can arise from many causes, i.e. a lake or a hard band of rock. In time all these are smoothed out to give a logarithmic curve. Largely a theoretical concept.

Basic Rocks. Rocks containing under 55% of silica. Also called undersaturated rocks. These igneous rocks are mostly dark in colour and fairly heavy. Consist largely of plagioclase felspars that are themselves often enclosed in large crystals of augite along with magnetite and olivine.

Breccia. A rock made up of angular fragments cemented together. Origin can be variable. The fragmentation may be due to faulting. Rapid denudation with little transportation can produce a breccia, and breccias are also formed by explosive phases of vulcanicity.

Brockram. A term applied to the basal breccia of the Permain.

Bryozoa. The sea mats or corallines. Animals which live attached to the rocks on the sea bed. Usually much branched and although they may superficially resemble corals are in fact more complex.

Cainozoic. Sometimes spelt Kainozoic. The latest geological era. Includes the Tertiary and the Quaternary. From the end of the Cretaceous to the present. Some 70 million years.

Caledonian. Named after the part of Scotland known as Caledonia. Applied to a series of earth movements in late Silurian and Devonian times. The present mountains of Scotland are the stumps of the mountain chains raised in that area during those times. The movement was widespread and affected Lakeland. The axis of the folds run N.E.—S.W.

Cambrian. A series of rocks well exposed and first studied in North Wales by Adam Sedgewick who called them after the ancient name for Wales, Cambria. They are the oldest sedimentary rocks to contain easily recognised fossils. Applied also to the period of time when these rocks were being formed. Approximately from 600—500 million years ago.

Carboniferous. A series of very mixed sediments. Limestones, shales and sandstones, but named from the large amount of coal contained in the upper part of the series. The Carboniferous lasted for roughly 80 million years, from 350 to 270 million years ago.

Charnian. Applied to a series of rocks in the Charnwood Forest area. Pre-Cambrian in age. Also applied to a series of earth movements that produced folds with predominantly N.W.—S.E. axes.

Chordate. A term applied to simple animals distinguished by a hollow nervous chord along the back where later the backbone develops.

Cleavage. A structure impressed on rocks (by pressure) long after their induration. As a result, the particles of the rock are re-arranged in such a way that the rock splits easily. The direction of cleavage is usually at a high angle to the bedding.

Conglomerate. A rock type composed of well worn, mostly rounded pebbles cemented together.

Corals. A group of marine animals of ancient lineage which secreted hard parts of calcium carbonate. Often found fossilized and most beautifully preserved. The older corals, the Tetra coralla, died out at the end of Palaeozoic times to be followed by the Hexacoralla from which our present corals are descended.

Cordierite. Sometimes called dichroite. A mineral of metamorphism.

Country rock. The surrounding rock. The rock penetrated by mineral veins of igneous intrusions. The existing rock through which a volcano bursts at the onset of volcanic activity.

Cretaceous. A rock series made up mostly of chalk. A period of geological time which lasted about 65 million years, from 135 to 70 million years ago.

Deposit. The material laid down as the result of erosion and transportation. There are many kinds of deposit depending on different conditions and the material suffering erosion, i.e. shore deposits which are often conglomerates; aeolian deposits, the result of desert erosion.

Devonian. A series of rocks first studied in Devon. This, however, turned out to be a marine phase quite untypical of much of Britain. As most of the rocks were formed under desert or near desert conditions they are predominantly red. Often called the "Old Red" in contra-distinction to the similar rocks of the Permo-Triassic. A period of geological time which lasted for about 50 M. years, from 400 to 350 million years ago.

Differentiation. The production from a common magma of differing rock types. A slow and complex process about which there is more theorising than agreement.

Diorite. A coarse grained igneous rock of intermediate composition. Dark in colour, it contains plagioclase felspars, augite or hornblende with much dark mica.

Dip. The slope of the beds with the horizontal as a datum.

Dolerite. The term means "deceptive" and refers to the many forms this rock can assume. An igneous intrusive rock. The intrusive form of the extrusive basalt.

Dolomite. A calcium magnesium carbonate. A rock which is mostly limestone but contains from 5 to 15% of magnesium.

Dyke. A form of intrusion that runs across country like a wall. Sometimes the country rock, hardened by baking, becomes more resistant than the dyke, then the wall becomes a trench.

Erosion. The destruction of the land surface by weathering. The term is often made to include the transportation of the rock waste.

Erratic. A rock fragment from a pebble to a large boulder transported by ice and left when the ice melted. Typically a piece of rock different from the underlying rock on which it has come to rest.

Extrusive. Igneous material poured out and consolidated. Lavas are extrusive rocks.

Fault. A break in the strata; a discontinuity; a displacement. Faults may be single but are more often compound, i.e. a major fault will often have minor faults either running parallel to it or branching off from it. There are two notable kinds of fault. Breaks in the strata due to tension. These are the commonest and are called "normal" faults. Faults due to pressure applied to the rocks are called reverse faults. A reversed fault of low angle passes into a thrust plane.

Fault Rock. See Breccia.

Felspar. Or to give it its old name, feldspar, is an important rock-forming mineral. Although the composition of felspars is very variable they are all essentially aluminium silicates. Orthoclase is a potassium-aluminium felspar. Albite, a plagioclase felspar, is a sodium-aluminium felspar. The only satisfactory method of determination of the felspars is examination in thin section under a polarising microscope.

Ferric. The highly oxidised state of iron.

Fireclay. The material composing the bed immediately below most coal seams. A fossil seat earth representing the soil in which the coal-forming plants grew. Because, by their growth, the plants removed all the elements like potassium and iron from this soil the residual clay can be used for making bricks which will stand temperatures at which bricks made from ordinary clay would melt.

Fossils. The word originally meant "dug up" but the term is now used to denote the remains, or impressions, of once living things entombed in the rocks. They vary from atom replacements which give in marvellous detail the original structure, to mere impressions on the rocks left by worms, jelly fish or the footprints of birds and reptiles. A careful study of fossils has told us much about the lines of development of living things, and about the conditions under which the original organisms lived. Because the chances of fossilization are so much greater in the sea than on land our knowledge of past life on this planet is overwhelmingly biased in that direction.

Graptolite. An extinct colonial animal. Confined to the upper Cambrian, Ordovician and Silurian where they are useful as indications of the relative age of the rocks in which they are found.

Greisen. A rock of late stage granitic origin. Usually associated with pneumatolysis. Consists mainly of quartz and mica with topaz.

Grikes. Joints in limestones which have been widened by solution.

Grits. Sedimentary rocks, the chief constituent of which is quartz. The grains are larger and more angular than the grains in a sandstone. Often contains decayed or fresh pieces of felspar. A grit with much fresh felspar is known as an arkose.

Gypsum. An evaporite, composed of calcium sulphate with two molecules of water of crystallization.

Helium. An element first noted in the sun. An inert gas and one end-product of radio-active decay.

Hercynian. A great mountain building movement which folded the sediments, beginning in late Carboniferous times. (Now become Variscan.)

Hornfels. An old rock term. A rock produced by metamorphism. A rock which is neither properly a schist nor granulose. Essentially consists of quartz, mica, sometimes a little felspar and minerals like cordierite and garnet.

Hydrothermal. A term applied to the heated waters given off as a dying stage in the cooling of a deep seated igneous mass. Many minerals are deposited by such waters.

Igneous. A general term literally meaning "fire formed". A bad word really, for fire, in the ordinary sense, has nothing to do with it. By common usage any rock formed as a result of fusion, whether poured out as lava or intruded as dyke, sill or laccolith.

Intrusive. A rock, usually igneous, which has penetrated the country rock.

Joints. Vertical cracks, usually at right angles to the bedding in sedimentary rocks. Roughly at right angles to one another in igneous rocks. In either case they may be due to contraction. Contraction upon drying out in the case of sediments, or upon cooling in the case of igneous rocks. They can also be produced subsequently by tension or torsion.

Jurassic. The middle division of the Mesozoic. Lasted for about 45 million years from 180 to 135 million years ago. This is the period of geological time when the saurians and ammonites were dominant.

Lava. Material poured out in molten form at the earth's surface issuing from a volcanic vent or fissure. Lavas are usually stony or glassy in appearance and contain amygdales. If the flow is very thick, or for some other reason has cooled slowly, the rock may be cryptocrystalline, i.e. made up of tiny crystals which can be seen with a hand lens.

Limestone. So called because the chief constituent is carbonate of lime. A rock made up of the comminuted remains of shells, corals, foraminifera and precipitated lime. Essentially a sedimentary rock which is often very fossiliferous.

Magma. Molten rock, often highly charged with gases, which is formed in the depths of the earth. The mother liquor from which igneous rocks originate.

Magnesian Limestone. Often referred to as dolomite. A limestone containing from 5 to 15% of magnesium carbonate.

Mammilary. Breast-like, a form taken by some minerals.

Meander. A pronounced bend in the course of a river. A meandering river swings from side to side and is then said to be in its Plain Stage.

Metamorphic. A rock which has suffered a change of form. Changes due to heat are spoken of as "contact metamorphism". Changes due to pressure by being buried under thousands of feet of other rocks are spoken of as "dynamic metamorphism", or alternatively as "regional metamorphism".

Mica. A common rock-forming mineral. There are many different kinds but all are hydrated aluminium silicates characterised by their softness and the ease with which they can be split into thin plates.

Misfit. A small stream obviously out of all proportion to the valley through which it flows.

Moraine. A term applied to material, usually clay and stones, left by melting ice. "Terminal moraines" are formed where the ice has halted in its retreat up a valley. Ground moraines, or drumlins, are the result of morainic material which has found its way to the floor of the glacier and then been over-ridden by the ice to form rounded mounds. All moraines are characterised by unsorted material, angular rather than rounded fragments, and often by striated pebbles.

Mudstones. A rock made up of consolidated mud. The bedding planes are rather irregularly spaced and the beds discontinuous. Unlike a shale a mudstone splits very indifferently.

Olivine. A complex silicate of magnesium and iron. Usually found as pale green crystals or splotches in basic rocks. A rather unstable mineral soon attacked by the weather.

Ordovician. A rock system named after an old Welsh tribe. A period of geological time between the Cambrian and the Silurian, approximately 60 million years, from 500 to 440 million years ago. The rocks of the central core of the Lake District are mostly Ordovician.

Outcrop. Where solid rock appears at the surface. Sometimes defined as where a rock WOULD appear at the surface if superficial deposits were stripped away. The second definition seems more technical than logical.

Ox-bow Lake. A lake formed by the cutting through of an acute meander.

Parasitic Cone. A small cone on the side of a larger volcanic cone.

Pene-plain. The theoretical end point of a long period of erosion. An almost featureless plain characterised by meandering rivers and a general low relief.

Permian. A rock system accumulated mostly under desert conditions. A period of geological time between the Carboniferous and the Triassic, it ends the Palaeozoic and lasted about 45 million years, from 270 to 225 million years ago.

Pneumatolysis. The last stage in the consolidation of an acid magma. A stage characterised by the giving off of highly active gases and fluids, the destruction of much felspar and the deposition of minerals.

Polyp. The fleshy part of a coral. A sea anemone is a polyp. Sometimes they grow singly, often in association. Some reproduce themselves by budding only, whilst others have a sexual phase. There is often a short free swimming stage which aids dispersion.

Porphyrite. A rock structure where isolated but well-developed crystals, often of felspar, stand out in a finer textured base.

Pothole. A limestone solution phenomenon. Limestone, a calcium carbonate, is readily soluble in water carrying carbon dioxide, or peaty acids. Solution widens the joints and produces more or less circular holes which may go down for many feet.

Pre-Cambrian. The vast series of rocks laid down before the commencement of the Cambrian some 600 million years ago. The later members may contain traces of organic material.

Pyroxene. A family of rock-forming minerals. Mainly silicates of magnesium, calcium and iron. Augite is a pyroxene. Found mostly in basic igneous rocks.

Quaternary. The last of the four great divisions of geological time. It includes the present. Approximately two million years.

Radio-activity. A process of natural decay found in some of the heavier elements which results in a chemical change. These changes seem to be completely unaffected by heat, pressure or any other agency. Uranium decays through many stages and over a very long period of time to end finally as lead. Of interest to geologists, because it enables definite time scales to be worked out.

Rhyolite. A volcanic rock of acid composition. Often shows quartz and orthoclase in a glassy or stony base. Usually light-coloured, it tends to weather white and show flow-banding.

Roche Moutonnee. A rock which has been over-ridden by ice and so smoothed and striated. Usually takes the form of an isolated rounded rock.

Rock. Geologically any mass of mineral particles or organic matter of natural origin. It may be hard and consolidated but need not necessarily be so. Geologically both sand dunes and glacial drift are "rocks".

Sandstone. A sedimentary rock consisting of small fairly well rounded grains of quartz cemented together. Special names are sometimes given descriptive of the type of rock or of the cement which binds the grains, i.e. micaceous sandstone, siliceous sandstone, argillaceous sandstone.

Schist. Metamorphic rocks characterised by abundant mica which gives a foliated appearance and a tendency to split into thin flakes. The mica may be muscovite, biotite or chlorite and be accompanied by other minerals such as talc, cordierite etc.

Scoriaceous. A cindery upper surface found on lavas that flowed subaerially.

Sediment. Detrital material which accumulates in the sea or in inland lakes. It may be comminuted rock waste or material of organic origin.

Sedimentary. That type of rock which originated as sediment. Characterised by being found in beds the planes of which are roughly parallel to each other.

Shales. A sedimentary rock composed mainly of fine clay particles. Splits easily into thin parallel sheets along the bedding.

Shatter Belt. A fault zone distinguished by much shattering of the rocks. Found most often in harder rocks that have suffered from intense earth movements.

Sill. An igneous intrusion in the form of a flat sheet roughly parallel to the bedding planes of the country rock.

Silt.-Siltstone. An intimate mixture of mud and sand. The resultant rock, a silt-stone, is usually harder than either shale or mudstone and tends to break into flaggy slabs. It often shows fine ripple marking and carries much mica on the bedding planes.

Silurian. The rock system between the Ordovician and the Devonian. A period of geological time which lasted for approximately 40 M. years, from 440 to 400 million years ago.

Slate. A rock which has suffered rearrangement of its constituent particles, and sometimes the formation of new minerals due to the application of pressure. A rock that cleaves easily almost at right angles to the original bedding.

Tertiary. A geological time term. From the Eocene to the Pliocene inclusive. Lasted about 70 million years.

Thalweg. A German term for a plotted curve along a river's course from its source to the sea.

Thorium. A radio-active mineral. Of importance for the computation of geological time.

Thrust plane. A low angled fault of the reversed type where the movement has been mostly horizontal.

Triassic. The first geological system of the Mesozoic. Often spoken of as the "New Red" for like the Devonian they are mostly desert deposits. A period of geological time of about 45 million years, from 225 to 180 million years ago.

Trilobite. Extinct aquatic animals belonging to the arthropoda. Their fossil remains are confined to the Palaeozoic rocks where they are used as comparative time indices.

Tuffs. Rocks formed from fairly fine volcanic detritus. The fragments, which are usually angular and small in size, may be individual felspar crystals in a ground mass of dust or volcanic glass.

Twinning. A phenomenon often seen in crystals where one crystal grows alongside of, out of, or at right angles to, another crystal.

Uranium. A radio-active element found in many minerals. Of interest geologically because of its use in assessing geological time from Uranium/lead and Uranium/Helium ratios.

Vein. A mining term applied to a body of ore of great vertical and lateral extent compared to its width, or thickness. Often, though not always, veins are mineral infillings along a line of fault. They are also spoken of as "lodes".

Vent. The opening of a volcano. The connecting pipe between the magma and the crater.

Vesicle. A steam hole in lava. When filled with minerals they are referred to as amygdales, and often contain zeolites or quartz.

Volcano. The rift or vent through which eruptions of igneous material take place. It may be a long fissure but more often it takes the form of a cone built around a circular hole from mixed layers of ash and lava.

Bibliography

Himus, G. W. and G. S. Sweeting. 1951. *The Elements of Field Geology.* London University Tutorial Press.

Holmes, A. (last edition). 1965. *Principles of Physical Geology.* Thomas Nelson & Sons Ltd.

Neaverson, E. 1961. *Stratigraphical Palaeontology.* Macmillan & Co. Ltd.

*　　　*　　　*

Eastwood, T. 1921. *The Lead and Zinc Ores of the Lake District.* Memoir. Geol. Surv. Mineral resources 22. 65pp.

Eastwood, T. 1927. *The Cockermouth Lavas, Cumberland. A Carboniferous Episode.* Summ. of Prog. Geol. Surv. Pt. II (15-22).

Eastwood, T., E. E. L. Dixon, S. E. Hollingworth and B. Smith. 1931. *The Geology of the Whitehaven and Workington District.* Geol. Surv. Mem. 304. XVIII pp.

Elles, G. L. 1898. *The Graptolite Fauna of the Skiddaw Slates.* Quart. J. Geol. Soc. 54. 463-539.

Elles, G. L. and E. M. R. Wood. 1895. *Supplementary Notes on the Drygill Shales.* Geol. Mag. 32. 246-9.

Firman, R. J. 1954. *Notes on Metasomatic Changes in the Rocks Adjacent to the Shap Granite.* Proc. Geol. Assoc. 65. 412-14.

Green, J. F. N. 1915a. *The Garnets and Streaky Rocks of the English Lake District.* Min. Mag. 17. 207-17.

Green, J. F. N. 1919. *The Vulcanicity of the Lake District.* Proc. Geol. Assoc. 30. 153-82.

Green, J. F. N. 1920. *The Geological Structure of the Lake District.* Proc. Geol. Assoc. 31. 109-26.

Harker, A., 1894. Carrock Fell. *A Study in the Variation of Igneous Rock Masses. Pt. I. The Gabbro.* Quart. J. Geol. Soc. 50. 311-37

Harker, A. 1894. Carrock Fell. *A Study in the Variation of Igneous Rock Masses. Pt. II. The Carrock Fell Granophyre. Pt. III. The Grainsgill Greisen.* Quart. J. Geol. Soc. 51. 125-48.

Harker, A., and J. E. Marr. 1891. *The Shap Granite and Associated Rocks.* Quart. J. Geol. Soc. 47. 266-328.

Hitchen, G. S. 1934. *The Skiddaw Granite and its Residual Products.* Quart. J. Geol. Soc. 90. 158-200.

Hollingworth, S. E. 1938. *Carrock Fell and Adjoining Areas.* Proc. York. Geol. Soc. 23. 208-18.

Jackson, D. E. 1961. *Statigraphy of the Skiddaw Group between Buttermere and Mungrisdale, Cumberland.* Geol. Mag. 6. 515-528.

Jackson, D. E. 1962. *Graptolite Zones in the Skiddaw Group in Cumberland, England.* Jour. of Palaeont. 36. No. 2. 300-313.

Marr, J. E. 1916. *The Geology of the Lake District.* Cambridge University Press.

Marr, J. E. & H. A. Nicholson. 1888. *The Stockdale Shales.* Quart. J. Geol. Soc. 44. 654-732.

Mitchell, G. H. 1956. *The Geological History of the Lake District.* Proc. York. Geol. Soc. 30. 407-463.

Postlethwaite, J. 1913. *Mines and Mining in the Lake District.* Whitehaven.

Rose, W. C. C. 1955. *The Sequence and Structure of the Skiddaw Slates in the Keswick-Buttermere area.* Proc. Geol. Assoc. 65. 403-6.

Walker, E. E. 1904. *Notes on the Garnet Bearing and Associated Rocks of the Borrowdale Volcanic Series.* Quart. J. Geol. Soc. 60. 70-105.

Ward, J. C. 1876. *The Geology of the Northern Part of the English Lake District.* Memm. Geol. Surv. 12. 132pp.

Index